Alan G. McDonald

SMALL BOATS
and
SAILING

By the same author

CANOES AND CANOEING (*Lutterworth*)
TACKLE CANOEING THIS WAY (*Stanley Paul*)
TACKLE TRAILER BOATING THIS WAY (*Stanley Paul*)
CANOEING (*Foyle*)
BOAT BUILDING (*Foyle*)
BUILDING AND SAILING CATAMARANS (*Foyle*)
SCOUTING ON THE WATER (*Herbert Jenkins*)
YOUR BOOK OF KNOTS (*Faber*)
Etc.

SMALL BOATS
and
SAILING

PERCY W. BLANDFORD

Drawings and photographs by the Author

LUTTERWORTH PRESS
LONDON

First published 1963

PRINTED AND MADE IN GREAT BRITAIN BY
FLETCHER AND SON LTD NORWICH AND
THE LEIGHTON-STRAKER BOOKBINDING CO LTD LONDON

CONTENTS

PLATES

PREFACE

WHEN you go afloat you immediately get a feeling of being right away from everyday worries. There is little of the bustle and rush of present-day life. As you cast off, your whole world is encompassed by the boat. For the moment you are master of your own destiny and your well-being depends on the way you handle the boat and its equipment. In few other ways to-day do you get the satisfaction of being self-sufficient. Life is simple and complete on board your own craft, whether it is a little dinghy or a sizeable yacht. Without necessarily going far from home, you can experience something of the sense of adventure which the older explorers must have had when they set foot in a new land, even if you have only gone across the bay or down the river. All of this in a boat you have built yourself, and you are having such a satisfying experience that comparatively few people can have today. The aim of this book is to show you how to build a boat and use it.

The boats described in this book are good, well-tried examples of their type, and are built in ways which take advantage of modern materials and techniques. Some traditional methods called for skill and tools beyond the reach of most amateurs, but the three boats described in these pages can be built by anyone reasonably handy with ordinary tools. The methods described are those used in most present-day boat building, so any reader who has grasped the techniques described should find that he can tackle very many designs published elsewhere.

I built my first small boat thirty years ago and have had at least one to use ever since. The number I have built myself must be well over a hundred. For the past fifteen years I have been engaged full time designing small craft and writing about them. Thousands of amateur boat builders have used my designs to make successful small boats, and they may be found in most countries of the world. Besides being simplest and cheapest to build, I believe that for many people, particularly young ones, the small boat offers the greatest pleasure. It is portable and easily handled, and it needs the minimum of attention.

The *Boy's Own Paper* has played a big part in the development of the building and use of all kinds of small craft. Like many others I learned to sail a boat literally with the tiller in one hand and the *B.O.P.* in the other. I learned a lot about boats from a *B.O.P.* book which is long out of print, called *Canoes, Dinghies and Sailing Punts.* The present book is in no sense a new edition of that, but with the companion *Canoes and Canoeing*, I hope it will serve the present generation in much the same way. To this end, the encouragement of the present Editor of *B.O.P.* (Jack Cox) is greatly appreciated.

This book is mainly concerned with building, although several chapters are devoted to using. There are very few books on building boats, but there are a large number on using them. It is my hope that this book will fill a gap in the literature of boating, particularly for young people. Those who wish to go on to more advanced use of the boat they build will find details of other books of use to them in Appendix B.

Because of the limitations of page size it is necessary for frames and other parts to be drawn to quite a small scale. These have to be redrawn full-size during building. Full-size plans, which remove any risk of error creeping into redrawing, are available, and I shall be glad to provide information about their supply if written to at the forwarding address opposite. Similarly, if anyone wishes to register a sail number for the Bermudan racing Wensum I shall be pleased to arrange this. Wensums are already in use for racing in some clubs. I can also provide information on the plans available for craft of other designs. A few addresses are quoted in the appendices. These are all expected to remain unchanged for some time. If any reader finds that an address is incorrect, or wishes to get in touch with a firm or official some time after the date of publication of this book, I shall be pleased to provide up-to-date information. I will also do my best to answer any boating problem at any time.

BM/BOAT PERCY W. BLANDFORD
London W.C.1
1963

SPECIFICATIONS OF BOAT DESIGNS

PETE
PBD 6

Flat-bottomed plywood-skinned single-chine pram dinghy.

Length	6 ft.
Beam	44 in.
Weight	56 lb.
Draught	about 4 in.

CORRIB
PBD 35

V-bottomed plywood-skinned single-chine stem rowing dinghy.

Length	10 ft.
Beam	51 in.
Weight	115 lb.
Draught	about 7 in.

WENSUM
PBD 32

V-bottom plywood-skinned double-chine centre-board stem sailing dinghy.

Length 11 ft.
Beam 56 in.
Weight (with decking, but without sailing gear) 135 lb.

Draught (centre-board down)	about 32 in.
Draught (centre-board up)	about 8 in.
Sail area (gunter rig)	66 sq. ft.
Sail area (Bermudan rig)	80 sq. ft.

Although the instructions in this book are complete, full-size plans are also available. Their use simplifies construction and reduces the risk of errors, which may creep in when enlarging the necessarily small drawings in the book. See Preface.

NOTE

The copyright in the designs in this book belong to the author. Readers may build boats to these designs without applying for permission or paying royalties, providing the craft are for their own or club use. Anyone wishing to use the designs for building boats for sale should first communicate with the designer.

Chapter 1

BOAT BUILDING METHODS

BOATS have been built in a large number of ways and all sorts of materials have been used, including some of the most unlikely ones. Throughout the years wood has been the most popular material and still is, but to-day it is available in special forms, some of which simplify construction and improve the boats built.

The earliest boats were probably logs, which may have been lashed together to form rafts. The next step was hollowing out the logs to form dug-out canoes. Where the resulting boat was not deep enough, the sides would be built up with planks, and the first step towards the more familiar construction was taken. An alternative method of construction used by primitive man was the framework woven or lashed together and covered with skin. The British coracle is an example of this. Its size was determined by what a single cow hide would cover. The Eskimo used the same idea, with seal skins to cover his kayak. Examples of these early methods may still be found, although they may be regarded as obsolete, but some methods whose history is lost are still accepted as good practice today. Building a boat by overlapping plants, known as clinker planking, was a method used by the Vikings, and this is quite common to-day.

Wooden boat building methods have to take into account the available sizes and shapes of materials. Trees grow comparatively long and thin, so that wood comes in planks of limited width, but in almost unlimited length. Wood has greater strength along the grain than across, so structures have to be made so that parts are supported

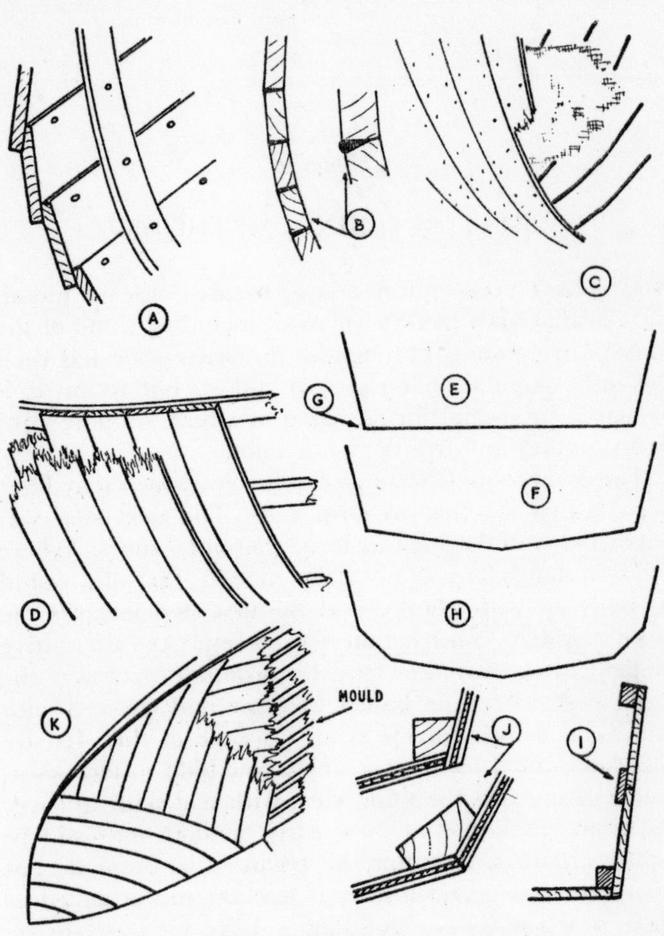

Fig. 1

in the weak direction by others crossing them. A boat may have its planking lengthwise, but inside will be other parts, known as frames or ribs, arranged crosswise. In plywood or laminated construction the various layers are arranged with their grains crossing, so that the resulting sheet has a fairly equal strength in all directions.

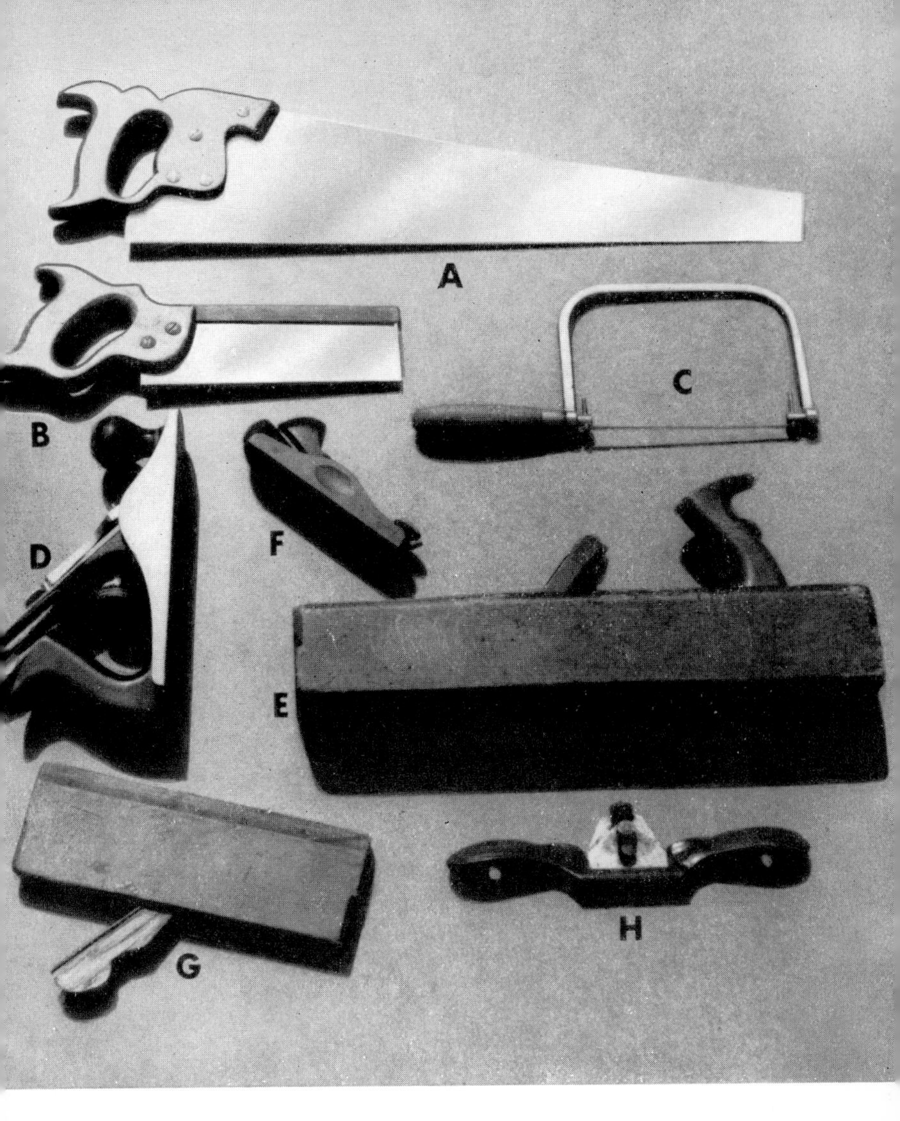

1. A. Handsaw. B. Tenon saw. C. Coping saw.
D. Smoothing plane. E. Wooden jack plane.
F. Block plane. G. Wooden rebate plane.
H. Metal spokeshave.

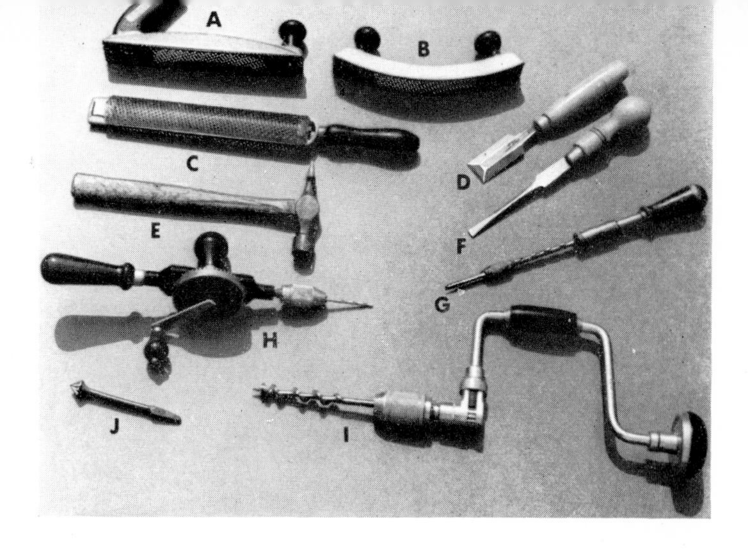

2. A. Surform plane. B. Curved Surform tool. C. Surform file with curved blade. D. Bevel-edge chisel. E. Warrington-pattern hammer. F. Plain screwdriver. G. Pump screwdriver. H. Wheel brace. I. Brace and bit. J. Countersink bit.

3. A. Try square. B. Combination square. C. Adjustable bevel. D. Marking gauge. E. G-cramp. F. Wedged cramp. G. Slotted wood cramp. H. Junior hacksaw. I. Centre punch.

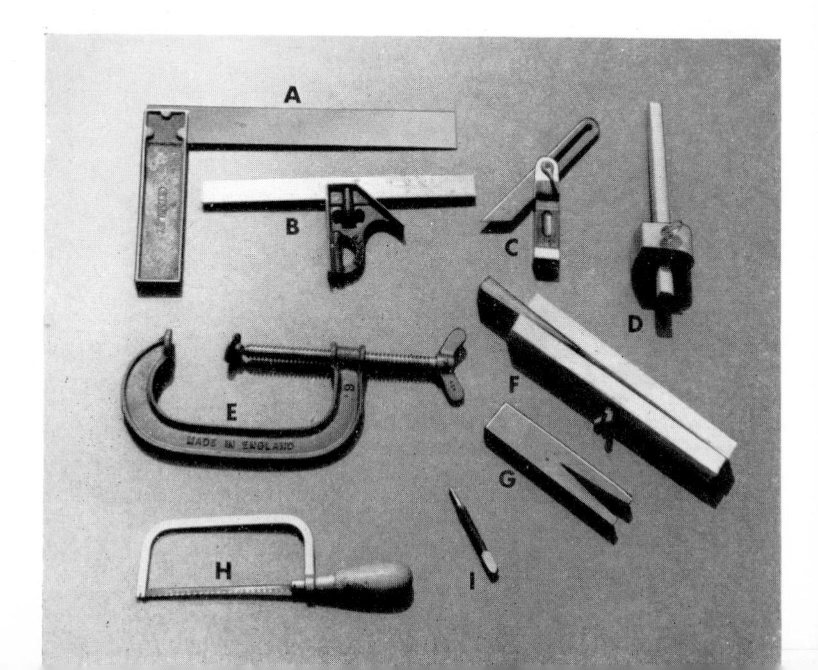

Wooden boat building to-day follows two main patterns, depending on whether the wood is used in its natural state cut into strips, or prepared in some way. Traditionally there are several methods of using wood in its natural state. All of these are still used to-day, but some of them require more skill than the average amateur is likely to possess. They may also require more tools and equipment than some of the other methods.

Planks laid fore and aft with their edges overlapping may be described as clinker, clench or lap-strake (fig. 1 A). In the traditional use of this method the overlaps are riveted at intervals and there are bent frames sprung into place to support the planking inside. More recent construction uses synthetic resin glue in the joints with no other fastenings, but this method is really only suitable for professional use when a series of boats are built on a mould and special facilities are available for quickly setting the glue.

There is an advantage in clinker planking in reducing the tendency of the boat to roll and in minimizing side slip on turns in a fast boat, but there are advantages, particularly in speed, in having a smooth skin. The traditional method of achieving this with strip planking is known as carvel planking (fig. 1 B). The planking is laid on frames in a generally-similar way to clinker planking, but each plank is made a good fit against its neighbour. The joints are not covered, but it is usual to caulk them. The outside of the joint has a V-form. This is stopped with cotton strands followed by a compound which seals the joint, but never completely hardens, so that movement or expansion and contraction does not cause leaks. Boats have also been built with the joints glued. Caulking is difficult and not very successful if the planks are thin, so this method to-day is more suitable for larger craft with planking at least $\frac{5}{8}$ in. thick.

Another well-used method in the recent past is double or treble diagonal planking (fig. 1 C). In this method the skin is built up of two or three thicknesses, with cloth either painted or treated with other waterproofing solution between the planks. The planks are laid diagonally. This permits the use of short pieces. Two skins may be approximately at right-angles to each other. If there is a third skin, it would be outside and laid fore-and-aft. In this method there is considerable strength in the skin itself. It either has to be laid up over a mould, which is removed later, or built on a framework which stays in place. This method of construction has been popular for Royal National Lifeboat Institution boats, but it is not advisable for small craft and is very costly for larger craft. For home boat building it has developed into the cold-moulded veneer method.

A method which achieved some popularity before the development of modern materials was the Ashcroft system. In this method a mould is made, with stringers giving shape, and this is covered with strips laid diagonally (fig. 1 D). The method differs from double diagonal in that the strips of both skins are laid the same way, but arranged so that the edges of the second lot of strips come centrally over those below. The lengthwise stringers remain in the boat and there are no frames required. With the development of synthetic resin glues and the availability of suitable veneers, which have made cold moulding possible, this method is largely superseded.

To cover a curved surface in wood involves using narrow strips. If broad pieces are to be used the shape has to be modified to suit, as broad strips of wood cannot be expected to bend in two directions at once, except to a very limited extent. As curves in the length are almost unavoidable, this means that the boat has to be designed with straight lines in the cross sections. In its simplest form this is a flat-bottomed craft with slab sides (fig. 1 E). The ordinary river punt is an example of this shape. If the sides are flared outwards and the ends swept up it is possible to have a reasonably seaworthy boat with a flat bottom, and some American dorys are made this way. It is more usual to have a V bottom (fig. 1 F). This is the cross-section of a great many modern boats and is generally called "hard chine"—the chine being the angle between the side and the bottom (fig. 1 G). To get a nearer approximation to the round bottom boat there may be two chines at each side, making a "double chine" construction (fig. 1 H).

When broad boards are used, which are too thin to caulk, the joints may be covered inside with battens. This is called "seam-batten-carvel" (fig. 1 I). Its place has been taken to-day by plywood, but it is a useful method when plywood is unavailable and in many cases it can be used for designs intended to be built with plywood.

During the second world war and in the following years, absolutely waterproof glues were developed. These are synthetic resins which set hard at normal temperatures and make a joint as strong as the wood. Normal wet conditions do not affect these glues. The outcome has been a revolution in boat building technique. With these glues it has become possible to make plywood suitable for boat building and to join boat parts more securely than hitherto. Marine plywood is available in large sheets, and modern boats are designed to take advantage of this fact.

A plywood boat can be built hard chine or double chine, with lengthwise strips to which the plywood is glued and screwed (fig. 1 J). This is the most popular method of small boat building to-day. For individually-built boats made by amateurs it is usual to build on frames which stay in the boat, but for quantity production it is possible to build on moulds, which are removed, leaving the skin with its built-in thwarts, bulkheads and other parts sufficiently stiff without frames.

It is possible to buy veneers of the same thickness as is used in plywood. Strips of these, with synthetic resin glue, are used to make the modern development of double-diagonal or Ashcroft skins. This is generally known as "cold-moulding" because the glue used sets at normal temperatures. Hot-moulded boats differ only in the use of glue which is set at higher temperatures. This method is suitable for large-scale production. The Firefly racing sailing dinghy and other boats by Fairey Marine are examples of this type of construction. Another large producer is the Chestnut Canoe Company, of Canada. Hulls made in this way are available for completion by amateurs.

A cold-moulded boat has three or more skins, each of which is made of veneers usually not more than $\frac{1}{8}$ in. thick. All of this is bonded together with synthetic resin glue. A mould has to be made in the shape of the boat. This is usually done with formers and lengthwise battens, assembled upside-down on the floor. Stem, transom and hog may be mounted in place then the first skin laid diagonally over the battens and held to them temporarily with ordinary office staples. Another skin is laid diagonally over this and bedded down in glue. The lower staples are withdrawn and more put in the second skin. A third skin is laid over this in the same way. When the glue has set the boat can be lifted off the mould and will keep its shape without any internal structure; being, in effect, a piece of plywood in the shape of a boat (fig. 1 K).

Glass fibre boats are becoming increasingly popular, but the method of construction is not suitable for the average amateur boat builder. Strictly speaking the boats are built of a glass-reinforced plastic. The glass is unlike the usual form, but is made of extremely thin filaments either woven or loosely knit together in the form of a flexible cloth or mat. The plastic is used in the form of a resin, in which the glass fibre is embedded, then the whole thing sets hard and rigid.

Before a glass fibre boat is made a mould has to be made in the shape of the boat. This needs to be accurate and with a smooth surface. When cold-moulding with veneers the mould used may have gaps and need not have a very smooth surface, but for glass fibre moulding the surface of the mould must be closed and smooth. Any imperfections will be reproduced in the boat. The mould is coated with a release agent which prevents the plastic resin sticking to the surface. The resin consists of several components which are mixed just before use. The mixture is spread over the mould and the glass cloth pressed into it then more resin applied. The usual mixture sets overnight at temperatures over 15° C. and cast in the form of a boat may be lifted off the mould. There is a snag in that the inner surface will be as smooth as the mould, but the outer surface will be rough. Although it is possible to smooth the outer surface, in production work it is usual to use this first cast as the final mould and repeat the process inside it to make a boat with a smooth exterior and a rough interior. All of this is a lot of work, which is hardly justified for one boat, but it becomes reasonable when a series of craft are to be made from the same mould.

A predecessor of glass fibre and cold moulding with veneers was the use of paper and shellac. In the middle of the nineteenth century boats were built by embedding paper in shellac over a mould and some surprising voyages were made in these apparently fragile craft.

Small boats have been built of metal, but it has never been a popular material. Galvanized iron has been used, but aluminium alloy is more common. The alloy must be salt-water-resistant if it is to be used at sea. Sheet material may be used, with single curvature over a framework, using close riveting and jointing compound. For compound curves special equipment is needed to obtain a satisfactory shape. Where the demand justifies it, boats may be pressed out of sheets in the same way as car panels. In the U.S.A. canoes are pressed out of aluminium alloy sheets in this way.

One of the simplest ways of producing a boat is by lath and canvas. To-day, the method is used for building canoes, but it is not popular for other craft. Usually there are widely-spaced lengthwise laths, held in shape by formers or frames. Over this is stretched a canvas skin. The canvas may be painted or it may be a special plastic coated fabric which does not require paint. British coracles were, and still are, made in this way. The original skin was an animal's hide. Irish curraghs (large rowing boats) are still made in this way.

There have been a variety of folding and sectional boats, but most small craft are rigid types which cannot be reduced in size. Sectional boats may be built in parts which bolt or clip together. When dismantled the parts may nest. The parts may be watertight in themselves or the sections may rely on rubber in compression or some other form of jointing to maintain their watertightness in use. In this sort of construction it is difficult to maintain a good shape. Usually the joints are all too obvious in the assembled boat's lines. Another way of folding is to have a rubberized fabric skin into which a framework may be assembled and tensioned, in the same manner as a folding canoe.

Some folding craft are really only semi-folding. Usually they fold flat, but remain about the same in over-all length. There may be rigid sides which spring to a curve when frames are fitted and tension a canvas bottom, or there may be a rigid bottom with canvas sides kept erected by struts. Sometimes the parts are all solid wood or plastic, with flexible material bonded to them, and the whole thing arranged so that the parts fold flat or spring into matching curves as the boat is opened.

There are inflatable craft, in which the main structure consists of air compartments, with a solid or fabric floor. As lifesaving apparatus some of these are very ingeniously arranged to inflate themselves when thrown overboard. There are also versions intended for ordinary pleasure use, but their making is not possible for the amateur with the usual equipment.

Chapter 2

BOAT DESIGN

SMALL boats are made in a great many shapes. While the amateur boat builder need not know much about design, he will find it useful to know the different types and the advantages and disadvantages of various forms. To most people the only shape for a boat in plan view is for it to have a blunt end and a sharp end. Most boats have that shape, but there are advantages in some other shapes.

The common shape of small boat is a "stem dinghy" (fig. 2 A), with a square stern and a pointed bow. If the stern is also pointed the boat is said to be "double-ended" (fig. 2 B). The advantage of a square stern in a small boat is in the increased carrying capacity aft. However, a pointed stern is better for taking a following sea, which it breaks and rides over. With the square stern a following wave may ride up the transom and enter the boat.

In very small dinghies the maximum capacity may be obtained by having a transom at the bow as well as at the stern. This is known as a "pram" dinghy. In a properly designed pram dinghy the bow board comes above the water in normal conditions (fig. 2 C). The name comes from the Scandinavian "praam" in which the planks all come to a point at the bow—the bottom planks coming up to join the side ones, without there being a stem post.

In craft larger than dinghies the pram type of bow is rarely seen, although some fast craft may have the deck built out squarely over a more normally-shaped bow. A larger pulling boat with a square stern is known as a "gig". The Naval "whaler" is a double-ended pulling and sailing boat.

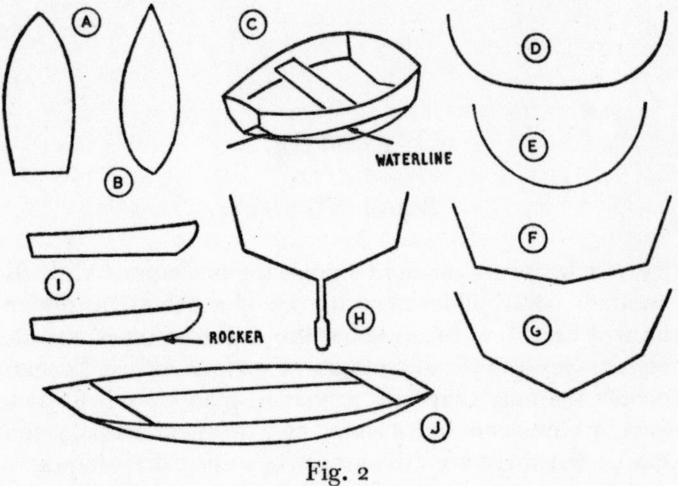

Fig. 2

Small craft may be built by any of the methods described in Chapter 1 and the cross-section may take any of the forms described. If the cross-section lines follow a curve the boat is described as "round-bottomed". If the central section has a fairly flat centre, like a letter D on edge, the boat will be stable (fig. 2 D). If the boat is unballasted and the centre section has a fairly even curve across the centre (fig. 2 E), it will be unstable and may be described as "tender" or "crank". Similarly, a hard-chine boat with a flat bottom or a shallow V at the centre (fig. 2 F) will be stable, but if the V is deep (fig. 2 G) it will be unstable. A heavy keel below the boat acts as a pendulum in relation to stability (fig. 2 H) and will prevent a complete capsize. However, it is uncommon for a small boat to have a ballast keel, which would need plenty of buoyancy in the form of air bags or compartments to support it in the event of a swamping. Usually the crew act as human ballast and trim a sailing boat with their movements. In a cabin yacht a ballast keel is more common.

Small flat or V-bottom craft have been known as

"sharpies", but the name is not so popular now and they are more likely to be called "hard-chine" boats.

In general form, both power and sailing boats have changed in recent years. For speed through the water, length is the most important consideration. Skin friction and the hull form also affect it, but speed through the water is related to length more than to anything else. The alternative to going through the water is to get, at least partly, on top of it. This is known as "planing". To get on to a plane the aft end of the underwater part of the hull needs to be comparatively broad and flat. A high-powered craft with this hull form will begin to rise, possibly around 12 m.p.h., and the fore part of the boat will come clear of the water, so that the boat is supported by a much smaller wetted area aft. A hull that could only travel at about 6 m.p.h. through the water, might easily reach 15 m.p.h. with only slightly more power, providing the power was sufficient and the hull form suitable to get it on to a plane. Light sailing dinghies with a powerful sail area are able to reach a high enough speed to get them on to a plane, providing the bottom is designed correctly.

When the boat is intended to take a high-powered outboard motor, its stern is very broad and the aft part of the bottom is almost flat. Without this, the motor would tend to pull down the stern and make a flurry in the water, but forward progress would not be great.

If the bottom is flat when viewed from the side, the boat will possess directional stability—it will tend to keep going in the same direction and may be difficult to turn. If the keel line is curved considerably, the boat will be easy to manoeuvre; but this may be excessive, making it difficult to keep on course as the boat will try to "yaw" (swing from side to side). A curved keel is said to be "rockered" (fig. 21). In reverse this is said to be "hogged". A hogged keel is never intentional, but it is a possible fault in an old boat. A sailing boat usually has sufficient rocker to bring the transom above the water. If the transom is immersed it will cause drag and make steering difficult.

In some parts of the coast a dinghy is known as a "punt". On other parts a large vessel is called a "punt". To the inland boatman a punt is a boat with nearly parallel sides and a flat bottom with the ends swept up (fig. 2 J). This sort of end on other craft may be called "punt-ended" or "swim-ended".

A boat with two hulls is known as a "catamaran". Although this name might be applied to a boat with more than two hulls, it is more usual to use it only for twin hulls and to call a three-hulled craft a "trimaran". A boat with twin bows blending off to a flattish single hull is called a "sea sled". Although sea sleds are not popular in Britain, they have been used in the U.S.A. to achieve rather higher speeds under power than normally-hulled boats. Sailing catamarans are the fastest sailing machines.

There have been a great number of rigs for sailing craft, most of them used on commercial boats in the days before power. On modern sailing pleasure craft the rigs are quite few and easily identified. Much of the development of efficient rigs has come about because of the research into aero-dynamics connected with aircraft design. As a sail going to windward is comparable to an aircraft wing in flight yachting has benefited as a side issue from work which has gone into aircraft design. Of course, there has been research into the efficienty of sails as well, and the modern approach to the problem of sailing is much more scientific than it used to be.

The simplest sail is a square-cut one hung from a yard (fig. 3 A). This was used by primitive man and was used to the end by most of the sailing merchant ships before they were ousted by steam. A square sail is efficient downwind but it cannot be used to sail very far each side of straight downwind—in some cases reaching was impossible (sailing across the wind) and sailing towards

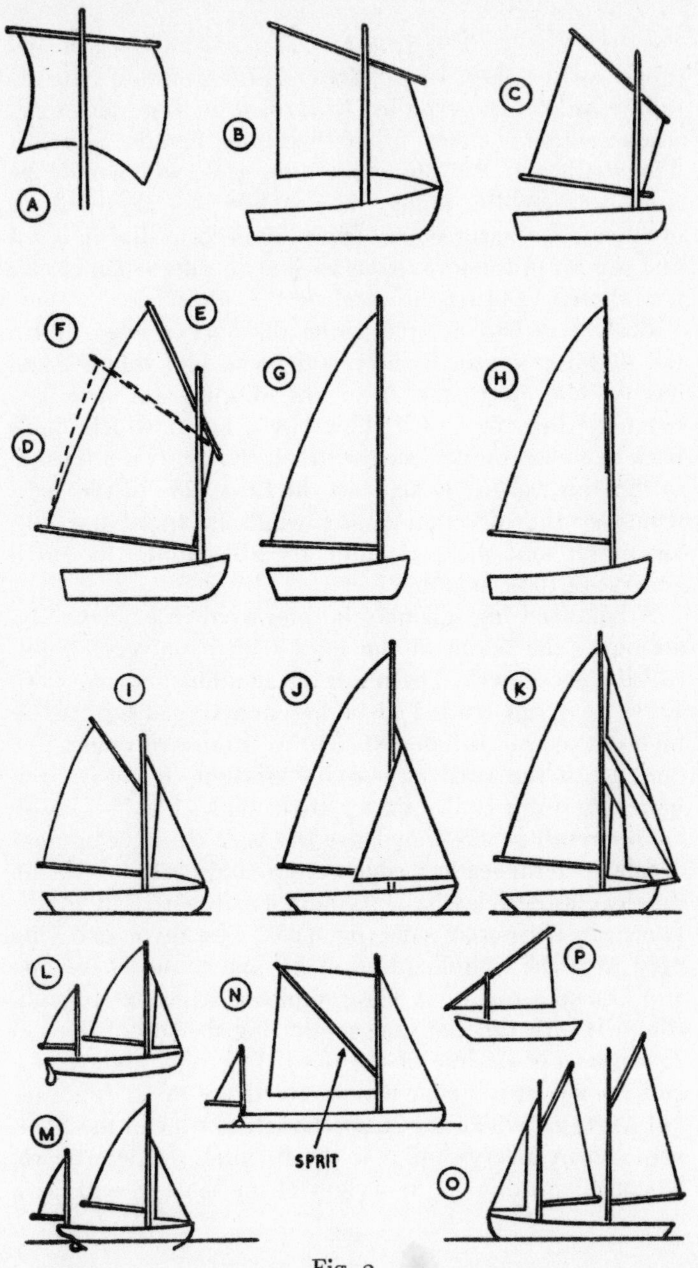

Fig. 3

the wind was unlikely in even the most efficiently rigged square-sailing ship. In smaller craft it was found that the square sail could be pulled towards a fore-and-aft angle, when sailing in many other directions became possible. The result was a dipping lug (fig. 3 B), which may be seen occasionally today, but should be regarded as obsolete. The name comes from the need to dip the yard and sail aft of the mast so as to change sides when course was altered to bring the wind on the other side.

Early sails had no spar along the bottom edge, but a sail performs better if there is a boom and this is usual today. The next step from the dipping lug was the balanced lug (fig. 3 C). This has a boom which hauls back to a cleat on the mast with a tack line. It is not usual to dip this sail—it is kept on the same side of the mast whatever the direction of the wind. Balanced lug sails are simple and cheap, so they are still popular for small general-purpose boats.

A balanced lug sail may be improved in efficiency by attaching the boom to the mast with a universal joint, called a goose-neck. The result is a standing lug (fig. 3 D). Early boat rigs tended to be low and spread out, but a high-peaked sail is more efficient to windward than a low one, i.e. if the yard approaches upright (fig. 3 E) it is better than if it is at a flatter angle (fig. 3 F).

One result of this knowledge has been the development of sails with the leading edge upright and nearly all racing dinghy classes today have triangular sails with long masts, known as Bermudan sails (fig. 3 G). This involves a long mast with the complications of staying it, and of stowing and transporting it. A compromise is a gunter lug sail (fig. 3 H). In this the spar supporting the top of the sail continues up the line of the mast. It is now known as a gaff, as a yard is a spar which crosses the mast. A gunter sail has spars which are short enough to stow in the boat, yet its form is very similar to the Bermudan. A gunter rig has problems due to the weight of the spars if used for a

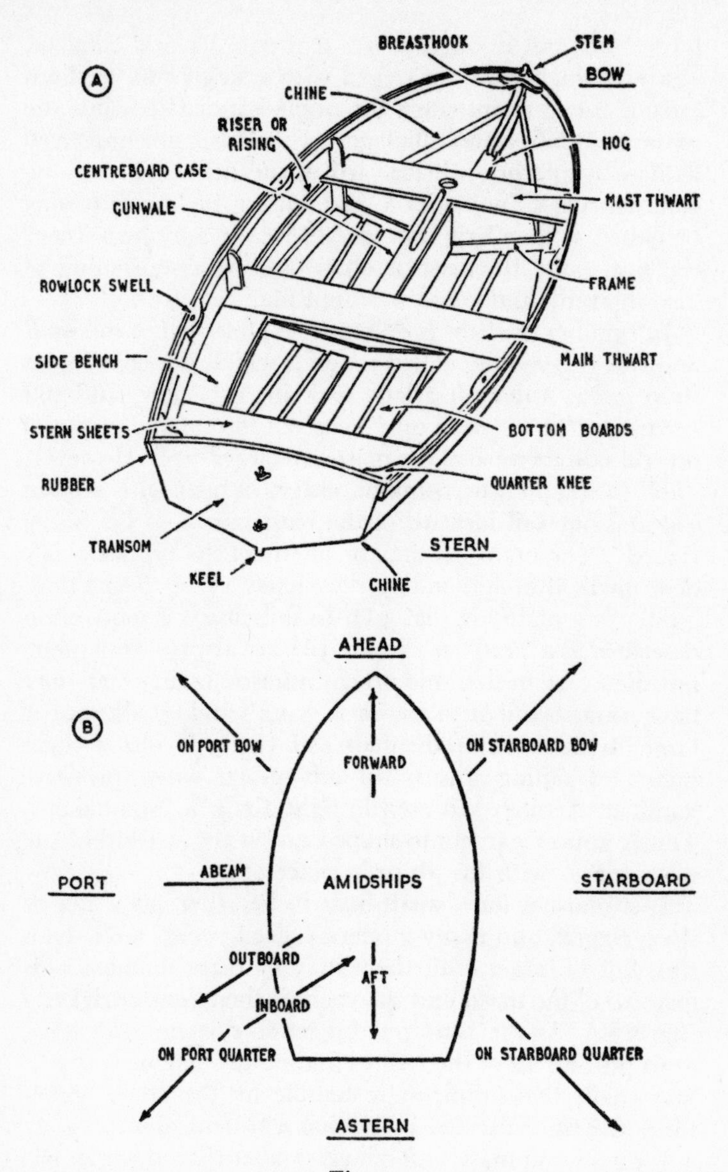
A
BREASTHOOK
STEM
BOW
CHINE
RISER OR
RISING
HOG
CENTREBOARD CASE
MAST THWART
GUNWALE
FRAME
ROWLOCK SWELL
MAIN THWART
SIDE BENCH
STERN SHEETS
BOTTOM BOARDS
RUBBER
QUARTER KNEE
TRANSOM
STERN
KEEL
CHINE
AHEAD
B
ON PORT BOW
FORWARD
ON STARBOARD BOW
PORT
ABEAM
AMIDSHIPS
STARBOARD
OUTBOARD
AFT
INBOARD
ON PORT QUARTER
ON STARBOARD QUARTER
ASTERN

Fig. 4

large craft, but in dinghy sizes it is popular and efficient.

Many small craft are rigged with a single sail, particularly if they are intended for single-handed use, but the manoeuvrability and efficiency of the boat are improved if there is another sail forward of the mast. There is no commonly-used name for a boat with a single sail. It may be called a "una" rig and in America it may be a "cat" rig, but today this term is often used as a shortening of "catamaran" and could be confusing.

In small craft there is only one sail forward of the mast and this is generally called a "jib", which is a convenient short name, although strictly speaking it is "fore sail" and the name "jib" should only be given to one of a group of several sails forward of the mast on a larger craft. However, "jib" is accepted by common usage. A boat with a main sail and one sail forward of the mast is said to be "sloop rigged". The main sail may be of any of the types already described, although to-day it is likely to be Bermudan, gunter or a plain lug (fig. 3 I). In this case it is more often described as a "gaff" main sail. Jibs are always triangular, but they vary in size, and an enthusiastic racing man may have an assortment to use in varying wind conditions. A large jib may overlap the main sail. (fig. 3 J) and on some points of sailing this is an advantage when properly handled. Another sail used in light airs is a "spinnaker". This is almost parachute-shaped and is set forward of the mast, either with the jib or in place of it.

It is unusual for a small boat to be other than una or sloop rigged, and many moderate-sized yachts have sloop rigs, but in larger craft there may be three or more sails forward of the mast, and the yacht is then "cutter rigged" (fig. 3 K). As the boat gets bigger so does the sail area, until putting all of the required area into one or two sails may make them difficult to handle by the crew. Sometimes the rig is divided by having a second mast.

If the second mast is aft of and smaller than the first, but set forward of the rudder, the craft is "ketch rigged"

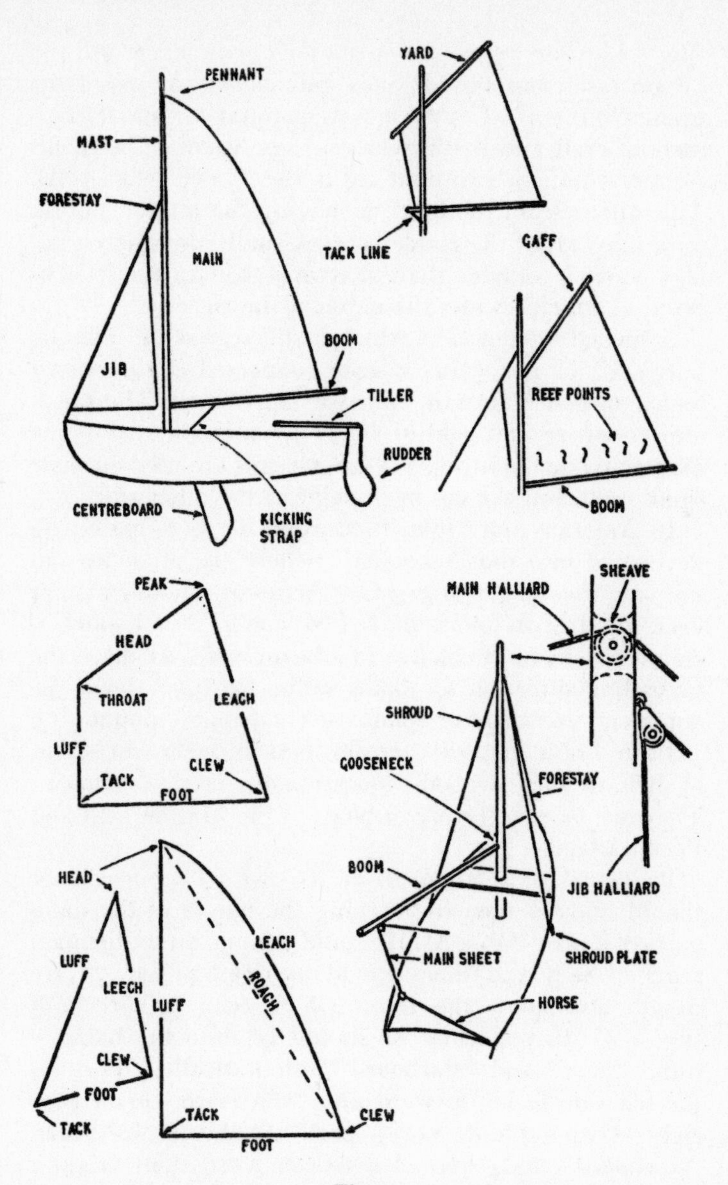
PENNANT
MAST
FORESTAY
MAIN
JIB
BOOM
TILLER
RUDDER
CENTREBOARD
KICKING STRAP
YARD
TACK LINE
GAFF
REEF POINTS
BOOM
PEAK
HEAD
THROAT
LEACH
LUFF
CLEW
TACK
FOOT
SHEAVE
MAIN HALLIARD
SHROUD
GOOSENECK
FORESTAY
BOOM
JIB HALLIARD
MAIN SHEET
SHROUD PLATE
HORSE
HEAD
LUFF
LEECH
CLEW
FOOT
TACK
LEACH
ROACH
LUFF
TACK
CLEW
FOOT

Fig. 5

(fig. 3 L). The larger sail on the forward mast is still the "main sail", but the aft mast and its sail are given the prefix "mizzen". Ketch rig was popular for small commercial craft and is still seen on some yachts. On yachts a more common two-mast rig is the "yawl" (fig. 3 M). This differs from the ketch in having the mizzen sail set on a mast aft of the rudder post. Usually the mizzen sail of a yawl is smaller than that of a ketch, but it is its position which decides the name of the rig.

A special type of yawl which is still seen is the Thames barge, which has a tiny mizzen connected to the rudder and a special main sail, called a "sprit" sail. The sail is almost square and held in shape by a single spar going diagonally across it (fig. 3 N). Sprit sails are used on some small craft, but are not as popular as the other rigs.

In America more than in Europe the two-masted rig developed into the "schooner", where the aft mast and sail are the bigger (fig. 3 O). Actually schooners have been built with more than two masts. A schooner is claimed to be most efficient in a beam wind. As this is the prevailing direction for boats sailing up and down the American coast, that explains the schooner's popularity.

Lateen sails (fig. 3 P) are also best in beam winds, but in Britain they are only occasionally used on canoes. They are more a feature of boats of the Middle East and Pacific islands.

Boating has a language of its own. The newcomer should make a start by learning the names of the main parts of a boat (fig. 4 A). He could then go on to the main parts of sails and their attendant rigging (fig. 5). He should also know the terms which refer to directions (fig. 4 B). In particular he should get into the habit of using "port" and "starboard" automatically. "Port" is the left side facing forward and "starboard" is on your right. As an aid to memory, "port" is a shorter word than "starboard" and "left" is a shorter word than "right". The shorter words go together. In the very early days of

4. How to hold a chisel for sharpening on an oilstone.

5. Removing the wire edge from a sharpened chisel.

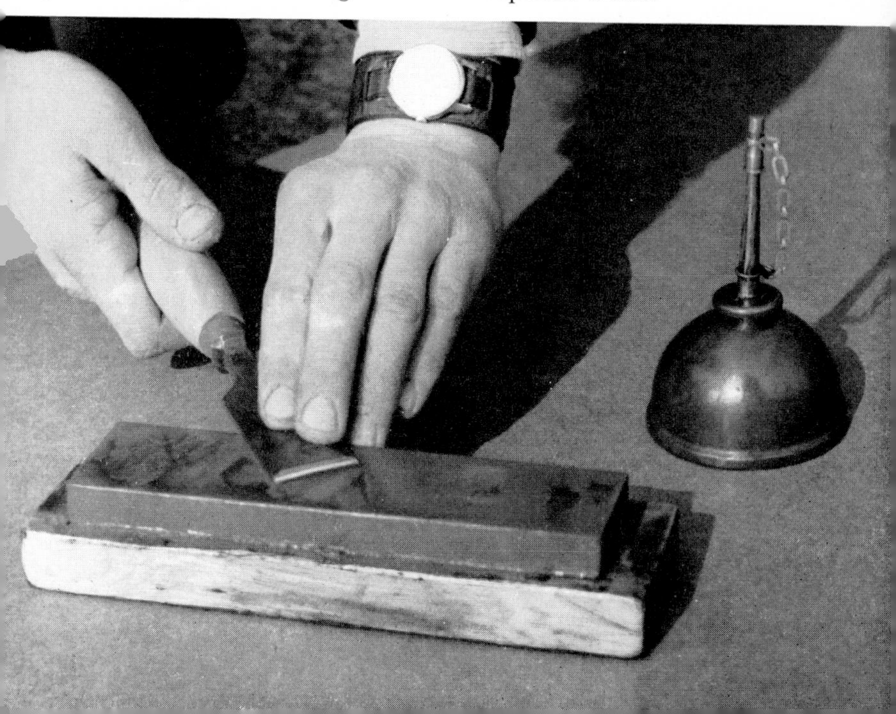

6. Pete: sculling over the stern.

7. Pete: rowing.

boating steering was done with a large oar. Because most people are right-handed, this was fixed over the right side of the stern. The oar was known as a steerboard and this became corrupted to starboard. Because the oar was fixed and would interfere with resting alongside a bank or wharf it was usual to load a boat from the other side, which was called the loading board. This became corrupted to "larboard", which was the name until the great era of sailing ships, when the two similar-sounding names were liable to be confused, and "larboard" was changed to "port".

There is no need to make a fetish of the use of nautical terms and ordinary language may be used for many things. The adoption of obscure or out-of-date words is probably worse than keeping the use of nautical terms to a minimum. However, the terms used in this book, and particularly the ones shown on the diagrams, are all commonly used and after a time the newcomer to boating should find that he uses them as a matter of course.

Chapter 3

TOOLS

MANY of the tools used in boat building are those common to other woodworking activities. Boats have been built with surprisingly few tools, and the amateur, who is not too pre-occupied with speed in building, can build plywood boats with just the basic woodworking hand tools. However, other tools will speed and simplify building. Some tools make accuracy easier to achieve. Others add to convenience and lessen labour. However, in building the small craft described in this book there is very little actual hard work and anyone should be able to build the boats with ordinary hand tools. With modern salesmanship and advertising it is very easy to be persuaded that some special tool is worthwhile, but its merits should be carefully weighed up in relation to the job in hand before buying.

Probably one of the most important "tools" is space to work in. Ideally, there should be a firm floor, preferably of wood, a roof to protect you and enough room all round to be able to work and manipulate the parts and assemble them, as well as room for a bench. In practice we rarely meet these conditions and boats have been built in the most unlikely places. We know of successful boats built in bedrooms, with the furniture piled at one side; in garages only a few inches wider than the boat; in sheds which only allowed work on half the boat at a time; and in the open, with covers over the boat between working sessions.

Building outside is reasonable in the summer, and the author has run successful boat-building courses in camp, but besides the unpredictable weather there is the consideration of temperature. Apart from the comfort of the workers, synthetic resin glue either sets very slowly or not at all if the temperature is much below 15° C.

In most boat building it is necessary to fix the boat down for at least part of the work. Consequently a wooden floor into which you can drive nails or screws is advisable. The alternative is a framework of stiff boards to which the boat parts can be fixed. With a small dinghy it may be possible to make the whole thing portable so that both boat and its foundation can be moved elsewhere for storage between working sessions. However, with a small boat, it is often possible to scheme the work so that everything that has to be done fixed down can be done in one working period. With a little forethought it is often possible to prefabricate as much as possible, so that many parts are made on the bench, with bevels and notches cut approximately. If everything is ready to hand, a surprising amount of progress can be made by two workers putting in a full day.

Most people who build small boats buy their wood already cut and planed to width and thickness by machinery at the timber yard. If this is done there is very little heavy work to be done and tools for cutting up and preparing thick materials will not be needed. In larger craft than are described in this book, parts have to be shaped in thick wood, and only then are power tools and heavy equipment really necessary.

Several saws are needed. Plywood can be cut from the sheet with a tenon saw, but most amateurs find a hand saw easier to use for the job. If one is bought specially, a length of 22 in. and teeth 10 per inch is a useful size (photo 1 A). This has rather finer teeth than many general-purpose hand saws. However, if there is a household saw already, that will do. Most cutting will be done with a back saw. This may be described as a tenon saw, if it is about 12 in. long or a dovetail saw if it is less than 10 in. long (photo 1 B). The important thing is that in either case it has fine teeth (16 or more per inch). Accurate cutting can be done with this, and the edge left will be good enough for many parts without further treatment with plane or chisel.

There are many curves to be cut. Broad sweeps can be cut with the saws already described, but in the thicknesses used in most boats, finer curves can be shaped with a coping saw (photo 1 C). This is rather like a small fretsaw with coarse blades. A jigsaw attachment for an electric drill may be used for the same purpose.

If the wood is machine-planed nearly all of the other planing needed can be done with a smoothing plane. Wooden smoothing planes are difficult to set and a steel plane about 10 in. long, of the size which most makes describe as No. 4, is preferable. This will have frequent use and is one of the most important tools in the boatbuilder's kit (photo 1 D). When a lot of wood has to be removed, a wooden jack plane (photo 1 E) is quicker than the smoothing plane.

Although not absolutely essential, a low angle block plane (photo 1 F) is useful for dealing with the edges of plywood and across the grain of other parts. In some methods of covering with plywood it is necessary to plane panels after they have been fixed partway across another part. This can only be done with a plane which has its blade the full width of the sole of the plane. Several planes of this type are made, and any of them will do, but the simplest is a rebate (or rabbett) plane, which may be metal or wood in various widths. Wooden planes (photo 1 G) are cheapest and quite satisfactory, and often available secondhand. Any width over ½ in. will do.

The traditional tool for smoothing curves is a spokeshave (photo 1 H), but the newer shaping tools are probably more use to the amateur boat builder. Best-known are the Surform tools, but similar ones are available in other makes. There are removable throw-away blades, covered in teeth, which fix to holders of various types.

They may be used in place of planes or files for flat and outside curves (photo 2 A), or sprung to a lengthwise curve for long inside sweeps (photo 2 B), or obtained curved in cross-section (photo 2 C), for other curves. A file or plane handle to take flat or curved blades and a holder with a lengthwise curve are worth having for boat building.

Not many chisels are needed, and any already available may do, but if they are to be bought, three should be adequate—one each $\frac{1}{4}$ in., $\frac{1}{2}$ in. and 1 in. The common type are known as firmer chisels. Bevelled edges (photo 2 D) are worth the slight extra cost.

Edge tools must be kept sharp and an oilstone will be needed. A double-sided one is worth having. The coarse side will remove notches and the fine side will produce a cutting edge. Use thin oil only on the stone.

The household hammer will probably serve for boat building, but if one is bought, the common Warrington pattern (photo 2 E) with a head about 10 oz. is more use than the heavier claw hammer. For very light work a pin hammer, of similar form but only weighing about 4 oz., is useful, although not absolutely essential. A mallet has occasional use, but much of its work can be done with a hammer providing a piece of scrap wood is put over the work to prevent damage.

There are a great many screws to be driven in any boat and good screw-drivers are essential. A long screw-driver is easier to use than a short one and the oval grip (photo 2 F) is more comfortable than others. The end of the screw-driver should be a good fit in the screw head, and for the most-used screws it is advisable to have a screw-driver for each size, with its end filed or ground to fit. A pump-action screw-driver (photo 2 G) speeds the work. A ratchet screw-driver comes between this and the plain type. Choice of screw-drivers is a personal one—what is important is the fit of the tip in the screw slot, otherwise there will be damaged work and frayed tempers.

Most drilling in boat work is for screwing. The metal-working Morse pattern twist drills are most convenient available in all sizes needed. They are most conveniently used in a small wheel brace (photo 2 H). Both this and the drills can be of the cheapest type—two cheap wheel braces are more use than one expensive one, as the two reduce the amount of drill changing. The cheapest drills are known as jobber's pattern. The expensive high-speed steel drills are more easily broken.

Larger holes must be made with bits held in a carpenter's brace (photo 2 I). Ordinary centre bits are cheapest and will be as good as the more expensive types for most holes in boats. A $\frac{1}{2}$ in. bit will be needed, but the purchase of other sizes might be left until sizes needed on a particular boat are known. Countersinking for screw heads is better done with a bit in this brace, than in the faster wheel brace. Use a rose countersunk bit (photo 2 J). In plywood this is better than a shell countersunk bit.

For measuring and marking out an expanding steel rule, which opens to about 6 ft. is useful, although a longer steel tape may be used if available. For shorter lengths a steel rule is preferable to a wooden one. It need not have markings less than $\frac{1}{16}$ in. A home-made wooden straight-edge about 3 ft. long will have frequent use. One of the most useful marking out tools is a piece of string. A taut string is straight, without any doubts, and for long lines this is a better way of obtaining straightness than using a board.

For right-angles a try square is essential. This may be the normal type (photo 3 A) although a combination square (photo 3 B) has extra uses in boat building. It is worthwhile having something to check right-angles larger than the try square will cover and a set square may be made from the corner of a sheet of plywood. Marine plywood normally has right-angled corners and an offcut may be made into a set square.

For the greatest accuracy it is often necessary to compare angles or make a second piece a pair to another, and the only tool for transferring angles satisfactorily is an adjustable bevel (photo 3 C). For marking widths the adjustable marking gauge is the tool (photo 3 D). The cheapest version of this is quite satisfactory. Where a line has to be marked parallel to an edge without scratching, a pencil can be used against the end of a combination square.

The final finish is usually given with glasspaper. Although there are several types of abrasive, common glasspaper is cheapest and does the job quite well. The average grade is marked "M2", meaning "middle 2". A slightly coarser grade is "S2", meaning "strong 2". The next finer grade is "F2", meaning "fine 2". Most finishing on a boat can be done with "M2" grade.

In boat building more cramps are needed than will be found in the average tool kit, in fact it is almost impossible to have too many. The ordinary G cramps (photo 3 E) in 3 in., 4 in. or 5 in. sizes are best, but for economy the simpler cramps made from strip metal may be used. There are several ways of improvising cramps. Two strips loosely bolted can be tightened with a wedge (photo 3 F). Light cramping can be done with a tapered slot in a piece of wood (photo 3 G).

Most boat building is done on the boat itself and a bench is not so important as it is for some other types of woodworking, but a stout table, or even a plank on trestles, is needed for some jobs, and there should be a vice of some sort. This may be a proper woodworking type, or one of the light type which cramps on.

A few metalworking tools are advisable. Although most fittings will be bought, there are occasional parts to cut or shape. A junior hacksaw (photo 3 H) will do most sawing. A 10 in. half-round second-cut file is suitable for nearly all filing. A metalworking countersink bit to fit a carpenter's brace is more effective than one intended for a wheel brace. A centre punch (photo 3 I) is needed to start holes in metal. Pliers and pincers have occasional uses.

A small portable electric drill can have many uses, although buying it specially is not really justifiable. It can be used for drilling for screws, etc. With a jigsaw attachment it will cut curves. A sanding disc on a flexible backing pad can be used for a number of jobs. In practice the many other fittings available for use with a drill are so rarely used that they are not worth bothering about.

Chapter 4

MATERIALS

MOST boats in the past have been built of wood and it is unlikely that any other material will supersede it in the future, particularly for amateur-built craft. There are a very large variety of trees and most of the timbers obtained from them can be used in boat building, although some are much more suitable than others. Choice often depends on availability—what is used in one country may be very different from what is used in another. For amatuer building in Britain the choice is usually limited to a small variety of woods if the best results are required. However, these are not always the cheapest and alternatives may sometimes be used to effect economy without seriously affecting the final boat.

Some trees tend to grow tall; others may be short and thick in the trunk. Some may grow rapidly; others may take a very long time to grow fully. Some may keep their leaves all the year; others may shed them in the winter. All of these things have a bearing on the quality of timber. If trees are packed close together in a forest they all compete in a race to the sunshine, growing long and thin, with few branches. Branches cause knots, so a forest-grown tree will have fewer knots in its timber than one which grew in an isolated position. The timber will also be straight-grained, as the tree will have grown upwards protected by its neighbours from the effects of high winds.

An isolated tree tends to spread outwards rather than upwards and it may be twisted and bent by the wind. The forest tree produces suitable wood for masts and those parts of a boat which have to be long and thin. The exposed tree can produce wood with naturally crooked grain which can be cut to suit shaped parts in a boat. Before the days of laminating these natural crooks were valuable pieces of timber.

In general timber is divided into hardwood and softwood. This is a fair description of the difference between the majority of them, although there are some softwoods harder than some hardwoods. Although the botanical differences may be more precise, hardwoods come mostly from trees which shed their leaves in the winter, while softwoods are mostly coniferous and have needle-shaped leaves which do not all fall in the winter.

The boatbuilding hardwoods are more durable than the softwoods, although for a boat which is to spend most of its time out of the water, it is possible to use woods which would not be acceptable for a boat being kept afloat. Softwoods used have the advantage of lightness, although some softwoods which are very resinous can be quite heavy.

The longer a tree takes to reach maturity, the harder and closer its grain. Some trees in this class never grow very big, so timber from them is not available in large pieces. Some of the hardest woods, such as hornbeam and lignum vitae, are only seen in small pieces, which are used for parts subject to wear.

Apart from durability and weight, sizes available are an important consideration. Wood from trees which do not grow very thick in the trunk may necessitate so many joints in the width of a board that they are not a worthwhile proposition. Another consideration may be appearance. A boat should be a thing of beauty. Its lines should be attractive. If it is painted, the appearance of the wood may not matter, but if it is varnished, a beautiful grain may do much to the appearance of the boat as a whole.

The most commonly used wood in modern British boat building is mahogany. Actually, there are several types of true mahogany and several other woods with similar appearance which are often loosely referred to as mahogany. The trees grow to a considerable size, both in height and girth. Knots are few and flaws in the grain are rare. Although these are hardwoods they are comparatively light. The colour of the grain varies, but most of the woods are the familiar reddish-brown colour, which has a rich appearance when varnished. Some mahogany, particularly Sapele, is difficult to plane, as the grain tears up in both directions. Honduras mahogany may also tear up, but Khaya is usually easier. When buying mahogany for boat building it is advisable to get it from a merchant specializing in the needs of boat builders and accept his advice.

Another wood used more in boat building than elsewhere is Sitka spruce. It is a very light straight-grained softwood, available in long lengths, although not in great widths, which is strong in relation to its weight. Most masts and spars are made of spruce, as it keeps down the weight aloft while being strong enough for the job and able to resist bending strains to a considerable extent without breaking. Because of its adaptability to moderate bending, spruce is often used for such lengthwise parts as chines and gunwales in small plywood boats. It is also used for light oars and canoe paddles.

Common deal is not much used in boat building. Much of the red and white deal available is of poor quality, full of knots and only suitable for the rougher type of carpentry, but for the smaller parts of interior joinery deal is satisfactory. Deal may also be used for the frames in small hard-chine boats. If straight-grained deal can be found it may be used in a similar way to spruce in structural work. Because of its cheapness, deal is often used for moulds and other temporary parts which will not form part of the finished boat.

For parts which have to be bent, ash is the most adaptable wood, although it is not very durable under wet conditions. It will take sharper bends than most other woods and is quite strong. It is a rather heavy hardwood, but as it is usually used in thin sections to take advantage of its bending qualities, the weight is not apparent. It is used for bent frames in round-bottom boats, and may be laminated to make knees and other types of brackets. It is also used for oars because it is flexible and resists breaking, but ash oars are very heavy to use. A better wood for bent parts in a boat is American rock elm, which is more durable, but it can only be bought in Britain from the specialist merchants. This is very different from English elm, which is a wild rough wood. English elm has been used for the planking of boats kept afloat as it has a longer life wet than dry, but it is less often used today.

Oak is not used much in boat building. The cabinet-making type of Jap oak is not used structurally in a boat, although it may have its uses in interior fittings. American white oak, which is a rather different wood is favoured for such things as frames and stems of craft larger than dinghies. Like American elm this is only obtainable from specialist suppliers. English oak is a very durable wood which is rather difficult to work, but it has its uses in keels and rubbing strips.

Teak is the traditional timber for high-class yacht work. It is very durable, has an attractive appearance and is very tough. However, it is expensive and too heavy and difficult to work for use in the small craft described in this book. Pitch pine is another wood often used for larger craft. It is a heavy softwood, with a very long life, which is used in larger craft, but which is unsuitable for small boats. Larch is a softwood used for planking lifeboats, but it is not used for small amateur-built boats. The various firs and pines have their uses. Douglas fir and Oregon pine are used for spars, but they are heavier than spruce. Parana pine has become a common wood, sold mainly for household woodwork. It is rather heavy and narrow sections tend to warp sometimes. It has a poor wet life and a moderate dry life. Despite these apparent drawbacks it is used successfully for frames of small boats.

In recent years several new woods have come on the market and we may yet have to get used to names which so far are unfamiliar. Because of this it may be necessary to obtain the advice of a reputable timber merchant when faced with a strange wood. Some less common woods which are suitable for boatbuilding jobs are: Afromosia, for planking; Agba also for planking, although it may be tricky to work; Iroko, with qualities similar to teak; Makore, with qualities similar to mahogany and suitable for underwater planking; Maranti, which is rather like mahogany; and White Seraya, which makes attractive decks.

To save hard work and ensure true surfaces, it is usual to buy wood machine-planed. It is important to specify that the sizes asked for are finished ones. Timber merchants used to supplying the house-building trade may quote the size before planing. The actual size after planing may be $\frac{1}{8}$ in. or more undersize.

Plywood used in boat building should be of a marine grade. The glue in common plywood is not a waterproof type, and it is liable to lose its strength in damp conditions. Fully waterproof glues are used in some grades of exterior plywoods, and in some places plywood marked "exterior" may have to be used for small boat building. In most countries a superior grade is marketed as "marine" grade. In Britain marine plywood conforms to a British Standard Specification (B.S.S. 1088) and this is marked on each sheet.

Plywood sheets are made in various thicknesses, which may be in fractions of an inch or in millimetres. There are approximately 25 millimetres in 1 inch and this will serve as a guide when converting. It is not usual to use plywood less than about $\frac{3}{16}$ in. or 4 mm. in boat building. Thinner plywood is so flexible that it needs plenty of framing to stiffen it. In most small boats $\frac{3}{8}$ in. or 9 mm. is the thickest plywood needed. Standard British sheets are 8 ft. × 4 ft. Other sizes are made and it is convenient sometimes to have longer sheets so as to avoid joints in the skin of a boat, but these other sizes are not usually obtainable from stock and may cost more.

Most marine plywood is made from veneers of mahogany or other woods of similar appearance. There are an odd number of veneers so that the grain on the outside surfaces is the same way on both sides. Plywood up to about $\frac{1}{4}$ in. is usually three-ply, but above that it is five-ply or more. Usually the veneers are of equal thickness, but sometimes the centre one is thicker. For most purposes this does not matter. When screws have to be driven into the edge of plywood the extra thickness of the centre veneer may be an advantage. The synthetic resin glue used in plywood is not flexible, consequently the more glued joints there are in the thickness, the stiffer is the sheet. A piece of three-ply is more flexible than a piece of five-ply of the same thickness.

Plywood suitable for use in boats is also made of fir, and this may be more plentiful than the red-coloured plywood in some countries. This is quite satisfactory. Red wood marine plywood is usually supplied with a surface without flaws in appearance and sanded ready for varnishing. For a painted finish it is sometimes possible to buy cheaper plywood of equal quality, but with flaws in the appearance which would affect varnishwork. Fir plywood is more difficult to finish on the surface to give a good varnished appearance, and this plywood is more often painted.

Ordinary hardboard will not withstand wet conditions and is no use for any part of boat building. The oil-tempered grades are water-resistant and they have limited uses on boats. Most makers of this grade prefix their trade name with "Tempered" or "Oil-tempered". Usually, but not always, this grade is darker than the standard grade. Hardboard is much cheaper than plywood, so its only appeal is really on the grounds of economy. It has been used for the skins of the smallest boats. Providing it is well supported by framing inside and protected by rubbing strips it will have a reasonable life on a painted boat which is normally stored in the dry. A dinghy to the design described in Chapter 6 covered in $\frac{1}{8}$ in. hardboard has survived five years general use without damage. However, it is not advised for the skins of larger craft, and in any case plywood is superior. Standard sizes are 8 ft. × 4 ft. The common thickness is $\frac{1}{8}$ in., but thicker boards are made.

Other boards of the plywood type, such as blockboard, are not made with waterproof glues, so cannot be used for boat building. Chipboard, which is made of wood chips embedded in a synthetic resin, is waterproof, but it is not generally accepted as a boat building material, except for interior joinery in cabin boats.

It is the development of synthetic resin glues which has made the manufacture of waterproof plywood possible. An earlier type made from casein had water-resistant properties, but it eventually broke down in damp conditions. Modern synthetic resin glues are fully waterproof, for all practical purposes. There are several types, but most are only available in quantities to industry. The glue is used with a hardener. Once the two have interacted and the glue has set, nothing can reverse the process. Of the glues available in small quantities for amateur use, one has a separate hardener and the other has the hardener incorporated. With the two-part glue, the glue itself is a white powder which has to be mixed with water to form a syrup. The powder will keep for two years or more, but when mixed into a syrup it cannot be stored for more than about two months. Larger users can buy the syrup already mixed. The hardener is a mild acid, supplied as a liquid. In use, the glue is put on one surface and the hardener on the other. When the two surfaces are brought together a chemical action takes place and the glue sets. Temperature affects setting time. With the ordinary hardener, the temperature should be upwards of 60° F (16° C). Other hardeners are available to suit other temperatures and to give quicker and slower setting times. With the standard hardener at normal temperatures, about 10 minutes is the maximum which can be allowed for manipulating a joint before it should be in its final position.

The glue with the hardener incorporated has a similar result in the set joint, but the method of use is different. The hardener is also a powder, already mixed with the glue powder. It is inactive until water is added. This glue has to be mixed into a syrup, but as setting begins immediately after mixing, only sufficient glue should be mixed for use within the time limit set by the makers. This hardener is slower-acting than that with the two-part glue and the working time is nearer two hours. Both types of glue are gap-filling. This means that joints do not need to be very tightly cramped or very close-fitting. However, the glue must not be expected to produce a strong joint when it has to bridge large gaps.

The standard synthetic resin glues are primarily wood glues, although they will join other porous materials to themselves and to wood. The set glue is rigid and cannot be used satisfactorily where the joint is subjected to much flexing.

The makers of the synthetic resin glues also make glues for other materials. One type available in small quantities for amateur use is an epoxy resin, used with a hardener, which will make joints in metal as well as many other unlikely materials.

For joints in flexible materials there are many adhesives, but none which is of really universal application. For rubber and rubberized materials there are the common rubber solutions used for tyre repairs and in upholstery. For canvas there are the black reclaim cements. For plastic materials there are special adhesives. For open-weave fabrics the latex adhesives are very effective. It is important to check that the adhesive is the correct one for the purpose, as many makers produce a large range of adhesives, often only identified by a letter or number. It is also important to follow the maker's instructions, as some adhesives have to be brought together wet, some have to be left to get tacky, while others may be better left until dry to the touch.

When something is needed to fill a gap without providing strength, a stopping is needed. For covering screw heads or filling cracks there are waterproof stoppings available coloured to match the wood. These are similar to plastic wood and can be levelled off after they have set. Where there is a risk of movement between parts the stopping has to be flexible. There are putty-like materials available, which are waterproof and which never set absolutely hard. Marine glue is a material with a misleading name, which is used as a stopping for such things as deck seams in larger craft, but it has little use in small boats. None of these stoppings has the same properties as glue and any strength in a joint must be provided by fastenings—they merely fill gaps without doing anything to secure the parts.

Most parts of small boats are joined by screws or nails as well as glue. Brass wood screws are commonly used, although in small sizes they tend to be too brittle, with a risk of shearing off when driven. Better screws are made of gunmetal, but these are more expensive and not so readily available. Ordinary steel screws will rust, so should not be used. However, steel screws are available plated in various ways to protect them against corrosion and these are suitable for some boat building purposes, particularly as they are much cheaper than brass or gunmetal. Cadmium plating offers good protection. Zinc deposited by galvanizing is too rough for screws, but bright zinc plating is smooth and satisfactory. Screws are described

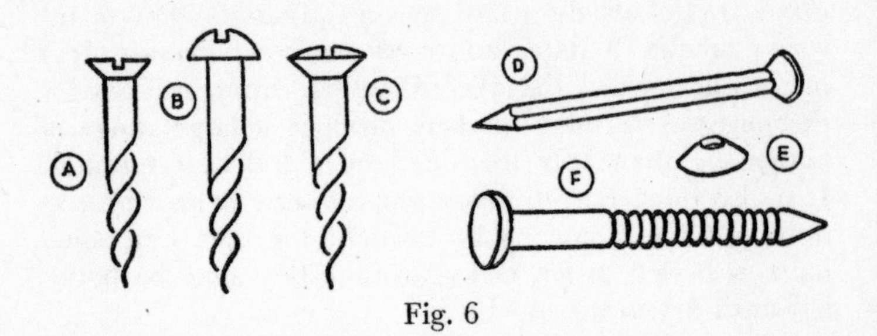

Fig. 6

by their length from the surface of the wood and by a gauge size. The gauge size is a special one for screws and differs from other metal gauges. Normally countersunk head screws are used (fig. 6 A), but round heads (fig. 6 B) and raised heads (fig. 6 C) have limited uses.

Traditionally, boat builders use copper nails with square sections and countersunk heads (fig. 6 D). For riveting they are used with conical washers, called "roves" (fig. 6 E). For fixing the thin plywood used for small boat decks, thin brass nails are often used. Nails with annular rings (fig. 6F), made from strong corrosion-resistant alloys, may be used in place of screws for many parts of boat construction and are quicker, particularly for fixing plywood panels. The rings grip the fibres of the wood securely. The table opposite shows suggested nail sizes for use in place of screws specified elsewhere in the book.

Other metals and alloys are used for fastenings, but mostly they are expensive. Examples are the various aluminium alloys and stainless steels.

Boats are finished either by painting or varnishing. Smaller boats are often varnished all over, but larger craft are more often painted outside the hull, with the insides either painted or varnished. Dinghy decking looks attractive when varnished, even when the rest of the boat is painted.

Most of the larger paint manufacturers make special finishes for boats. Conditions afloat are very different from those ashore and many household paints are unsuitable for use on boats. The paint manufacturers issue booklets giving advice on the use of their paints on boats and one of these should be obtained and studied.

Marine varnishes are nearly all synthetic to-day. These are easier to use than the traditional varnishes made from natural lacs, which were very susceptible to changes in temperature and humidity during application.

Paints are made in a number of types according to their application on the boat. There are special paints for bilges, decks, bottoms, etc., as well as the general paints for hulls. Wood has to be prepared by painting with priming paint. Ordinary household priming does not provide a good enough base for marine paints. This is followed by undercoats, which are matched to the top coats. Ordinary modern synthetic marine paints are all that are needed for most small boats, but for the toughest and most durable finishes there are the more expensive polyurethane paints and varnishes. These have to be mixed just before use and they set in a rather similar way to synthetic resin glue. They are quick-drying and make a much more waterproof skin than normal finishes.

Wooden boats are sometimes sheathed with glass fibre, or the seams of a hard chine boat may be reinforced with glass fibre tape. The process consists of coating the wood with a synthetic resin mixture, into which the glass cloth or mat is embedded. All the materials should be bought from a firm specializing in this work, as it is important that they should match. Their instructions should be followed exactly, as an error can be a costly mistake.

Annular ring nails as alternatives to screws

Screw	—	Nails
$\frac{5}{8}$ in. × 4 g	—	$\frac{3}{4}$ in. or $\frac{7}{8}$ in. × 14 g
$\frac{3}{4}$ in. × 6 g	—	$\frac{7}{8}$ in. × 12 g
$1\frac{1}{4}$ in. × 6 g	—	$1\frac{1}{2}$ in. × 10 g
2 in. × 8 g	—	$2\frac{1}{4}$ in. × 8 g

Chapter 5

BOAT BUILDING PROCESSES

THERE are a number of jobs which are the same in the building of most boats. Once these processes are mastered, boat building goes ahead quickly. The first boat may take some time to build as you feel your way, but later boats can be built much more quickly as you have acquired new skills and have the confidence to get on with the work speedily and efficiently.

Many boats are built upside-down on the floor. The first job is to mark out the floor so that the boat is set up truly and correctly. With some designs it is necessary to first set out the lines full-size. All of this is straightforward geometry, but as it is big, the ordinary drawing board methods cannot be used. Lines are long and angles have to be checked at considerable distances from the corner, if accuracy is to be maintained. It is most important that lines intended to be at right-angles should be so, to a reasonable degree of precision.

Straight lines up to perhaps 6 ft. can be drawn along the edge of a board. Lines longer than this are better "struck" with a chalk-line. This is a piece of thin string or stout thread. Crochet cotton is a very suitable material, being strong and fine. To strike a line, one end of the chalk line is either held down or tied to an awl pushed into the floor. You walk backwards from this rubbing chalk on the string. Use ordinary stick chalk, but avoid jerking the string. Stretch it and hold it down with your thumb. Either reach back towards the centre or get an assistant to lift the line a few inches and let it spring back. This will deposit a straight thin line of chalk on the floor (fig. 7 A).

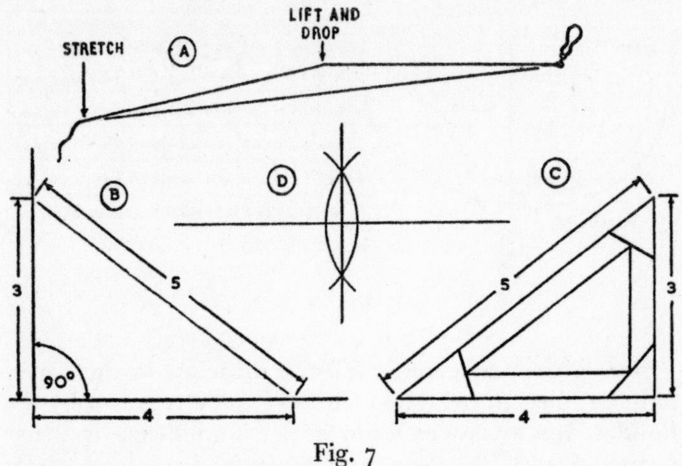

Fig. 7

Sheets of plywood can usually be relied on to be cut squarely by the makers, so the corner of a sheet can be used as a try square to mark lines at right-angles to the base line up to a length of 4 ft. This is usually as big a capacity as is likely to be needed for laying out the floor for a small boat. However, it is safest to check the squareness of the chosen sheet of plywood. This can be done by using the well-known geometrical fact that in a triangle with the sides in the proportion 3, 4, 5, the angle between the two shorter sides must be a right-angle. On the sheet measure 3 ft. and 4 ft. from a corner and check that the distance between these points on the edges is 5 ft. (fig. 7 B). Alternatively, make a set square from strips, using the 3, 4, 5 method (fig. 7 C).

There are several geometrical ways of marking out a right-angle. One way is to use a strip of wood and an awl as a compass to make two arcs, so that a line may be struck through their crossings (fig. 7 D).

When the centre-line or base-line has been struck and you have one line drawn at right-angles to it, all other lines should be drawn by measuring from them.

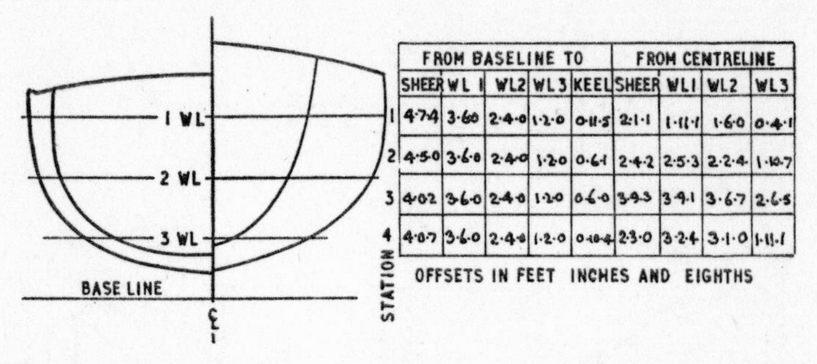

Station	From baseline to: Sheer	WL 1	WL2	WL3	Keel	From centreline: Sheer	WL1	WL2	WL3
1	4·7·4	3·6·0	2·4·0	1·2·0	0·11·5	2·1·1	1·11·1	1·6·0	0·4·1
2	4·5·0	3·6·0	2·4·0	1·2·0	0·6·1	2·4·2	2·5·3	2·2·4	1·10·7
3	4·0·2	3·6·0	2·4·0	1·2·0	0·6·0	3·9·3	3·9·1	3·6·7	2·6·5
4	4·0·7	3·6·0	2·4·0	1·2·0	0·10·4	2·3·0	3·2·4	3·1·0	1·11·1

OFFSETS IN FEET INCHES AND EIGHTHS

Fig. 8

Boat plans may contain full-size drawings or there may only be small drawings which have to be redrawn by the builder. It is always easier to work from full-size drawings provided with the plan and there is no risk of errors creeping in, as they might when making your own full-size drawings. Because of the limitations of page size there are drawings in this book which may be scaled up, but for all of them full-size drawings are also available (see Preface).

For a section which consists of straight lines the designer may provide a table of offsets instead of a drawing for scaling up. The table is drawn up so as to give the position of each point in relation to a base-line and a centre-line. The table may be made in ordinary inches and fractions, or sometimes measurements are given in three figures, representing feet, inches and eighths of an inch (fig. 8). To use a table of offsets, work directly either on a sheet of hardboard or plywood. Have a straight edge to the sheet and a line at right-angles to it, then measure from these datums. For frames, which are symmetrical, it may be sufficient to only set out half a drawing. The frame can be made about a centre-line.

If curves have to be drawn up from a small drawing, key points may be located by measurements, but the general shape can be redrawn using a pattern of squares. Use squares of a convenient size on the scale drawing and

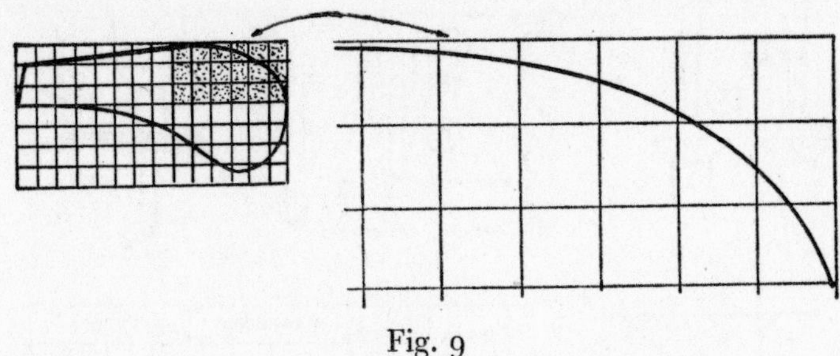

Fig. 9

others proportionately bigger on the full-size drawing (fig. 9). Sometimes the designer draws the small squares and indicates what size to redraw them to make the full-size drawing. If the parts are first set out at the points where they cross the lines, then joined up freehand, the final drawing should finish reasonably near the shape the designer intended.

The best way to transfer a full-size drawing to a sheet of plywood is by using carbon paper, following round with a pencil. Hold the paper down with weights or drawing pins. A comparatively small piece of carbon paper may be used if it is moved around without moving the drawing paper. Another way is to use a sharp point to prick through the drawing on to the plywood. The points have to be joined up by pencil afterwards. If the drawing is of a frame or other part which has to be built up from strip wood, the drawing should be fastened down to a flat surface and the parts assembled over it.

Much of the assembly work is done with screws. The screw-drivers should fit the slots. It is worthwhile spending some time filing or grinding blades to fit the screws mostly used. Take care that the ends are not rounded (fig. 10 A), but have flat slopes to square ends which are not too slack a fit in the screw slots (fig. 10 B).

A screw holds two parts together by pulling the upper part against the other, compressing the joint between the underside of the screw head and the pull of the threaded

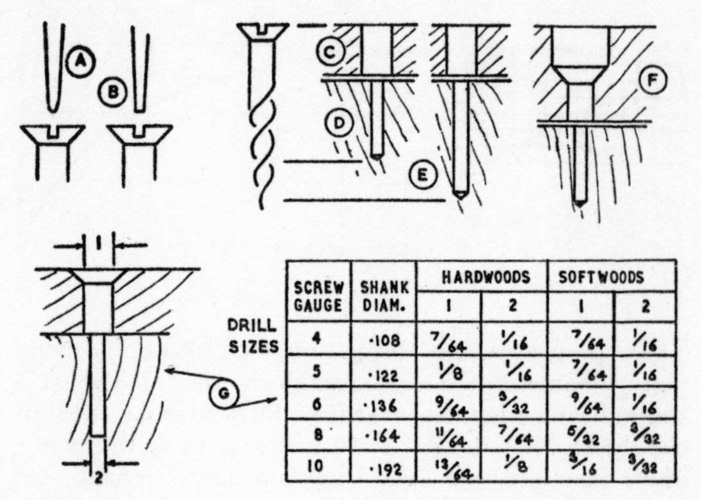

SCREW GAUGE	SHANK DIAM.	HARDWOODS		SOFTWOODS	
		1	2	1	2
4	·108	7/64	1/16	7/64	1/16
5	·122	1/8	1/16	7/64	1/16
6	·136	9/64	3/32	9/64	1/16
8	·164	11/64	7/64	5/32	3/32
10	·192	13/64	1/8	3/16	3/32

Fig. 10

portion. Consequently, the hole in the upper part should not be tight on the neck of the screw (fig. 10 C). There should be a hole in the lower part to take the screwed portion. Its size depends on the wood. Small screws in soft wood may be started with a bradawl hole. Larger screws in soft wood may need a hole drilled part way (fig. 10 D). In hard wood the hole may have to be slightly bigger and taken deeper (fig. 10 E).

In many woods a small countersunk screw head will pull in flush. It may in plywood. It is advisable to test on scrap wood before using a countersink bit. If a bit is used to countersink a hole where the head would have pulled in, the head may actually go farther into the wood than was intended. For larger screws, countersinking, at least part way, is advisable. With metal fittings, round headed screws may look best, or if countersunk heads are used, it may be necessary to countersink more than the makers have done—a screw head proud of the surface can be dangerous to hands or sails.

Sometimes the screw is buried and the head covered

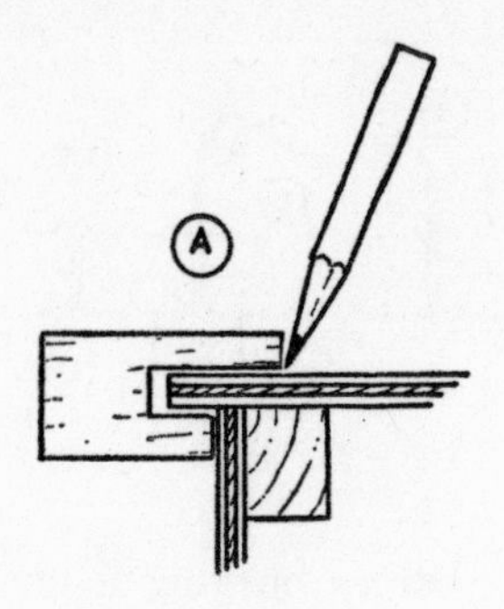

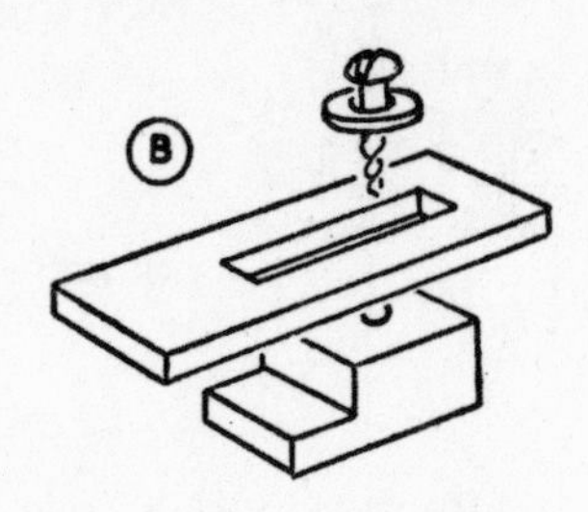

Fig. 11

with a wooden plug or stopping. This is done by counter-boring with a drill as large as the head (fig. 10 F). There are combination drills which make both sizes of hole for the screw as well as countersink or counterbore for the head, but these only suit particular sizes of screw and several may be needed on a boat. It is more usual to use separate drills. The table gives sizes to suit common screws (fig. 10 G).

The smallest sizes of nails may be driven without previous drilling. Galvanized iron nails are stiff enough to resist bending when driven, but copper, and to a lesser extent brass and alloy, nails bend too readily, so that it is usual to drill for them. For the thicker nails, in any case, undersize holes should be drilled, at least part way.

Screws or nails often have to be entered before an edge is finally trimmed. If the final pattern of nail heads is to be neat, a line should be drawn parallel with the final edge. To get over the projecting edge of plywood, a simple pencil gauge can be made (fig. 11 A). A more elaborate pattern, which can be adjusted, will suit any boat (fig. 11 B).

Nails can be used on thin parts if they are driven through and clenched. The simplest way is to merely knock over the projecting end while an iron block is held against the head. It is better to bend the point first by

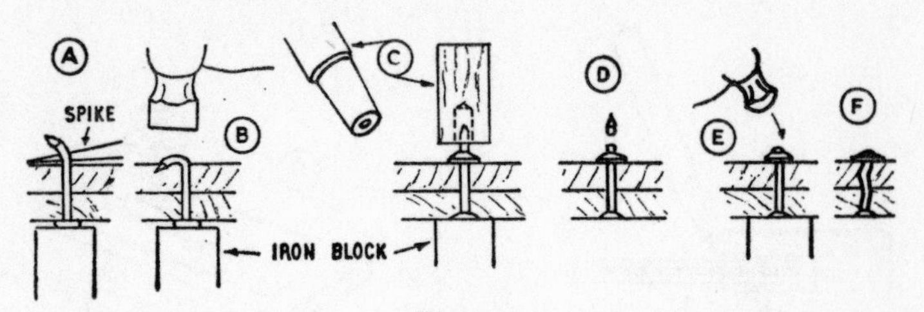

Fig. 12

hammering over a spike (fig. 12 A) before burying it in the wood (fig. 12 B).

Copper boat nails lend themselves to a method of riveting through roves. Although fewer boats are now built with all of the planking fixed by riveting, it is worthwhile mastering the technique as there are some parts in most boats which are best fastened in this way. A copper nail is driven through an undersize hole, then the head supported by a hammer or an iron block. A rove is a conical washer with a hole just too small to slide over the end of the nail without force. It is put on the point and forced down, either with a hollow punch or a piece of wood used on the end grain (fig. 12 C). The nail is cut off a short distance above the rove (fig. 12 D), using cutting pliers or side cutters, then riveted over the rove (fig. 12 E) with light blows from a light hammer. Light work is important, as heavy blows would bend the nail in the thickness of the wood (fig. 12 F). Under strain this might straighten out, making a loose joint. A ball pein hammer is best, but in awkward positions the cross pein of an ordinary hammer is better. With metal fittings it may be possible to dispense with the rove, if the end of the nail can be riveted on the fitting.

Sometimes wood or plywood has to be made up in the length. Strips may be lengthened by a simple splice made with synthetic resin glue. Within reason, the longer the angle of the splice, the stronger it will be. It should be at least eight times the thickness of the wood—on $\frac{1}{2}$ in.

wood at least 4 in. long. To get the angles of both parts the same they can be planed together without any marking out. Arrange them over the end of the bench with the parts staggered by the amount of the splice (fig. 13 A), then plane the two thicknesses together until they are brought down to feather edges (fig. 13 B). If nail holes will not matter, the parts can be glued and left with two temporary nails into a flat piece of scrap wood. Paper under the joint will prevent it sticking to the scrap wood (fig. 13 C). Alternatively, cramp the parts between scrap wood and paper (fig. 13 D). The nailing method allows easier lining up of the two parts.

Sheets of plywood may be joined by a similar splice or scarf, but the work becomes increasingly difficult as the length of the joint increases. With thin plywood it is very important that it should be supported on an absolutely flat surface while planing. Thick plywood may be stiff enough to stay flat despite irregularities below it. When gluing a broad scarf in plywood it is important that pressure is applied fairly evenly across the joint. Cramps cannot reach far from the edges. If two stout pieces of wood are planed with slightly convex curves, cramping at the edges will also press at the middle (fig. 13 E).

It is simpler to join plywood panels with butt straps inside the boat. This is quite satisfactory and easier for most people to do. Scarfing has to be done before the plywood is fitted to the boat, but butt joints can be made in position. The two edges merely butt against each other and both are fastened to a covering piece inside. The joint cover or butt strap may be a separate piece or it can be a thickened edge of a frame or other structural part. If the cover is independent of internal structure it should be reasonably wide. With a narrow strap on a curved surface, there is a tendency to show a slight kink on the joint. How the joint is fastened depends on the thickness of the plywood. A thin piece, say up to $\frac{1}{4}$ in. thick, can have nails driven through and clenched (fig. 13 F). Thicker

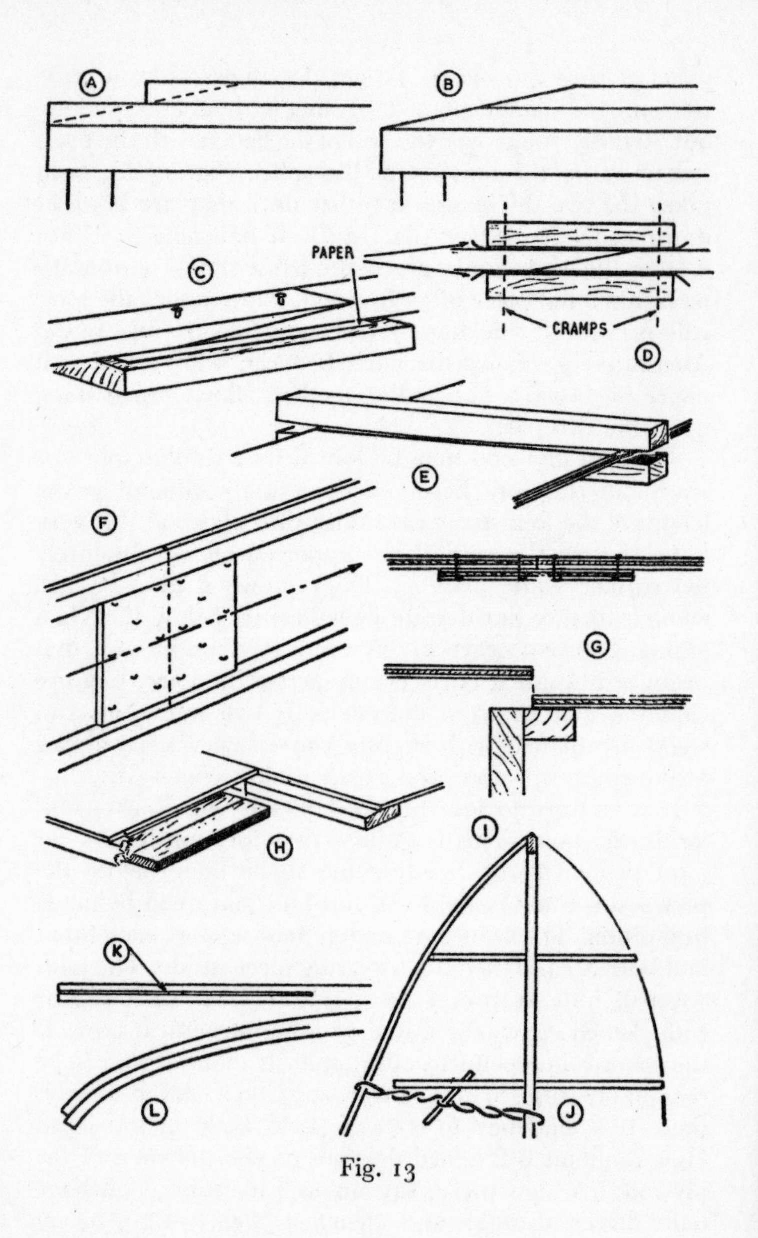

Fig. 13

plywood may take screws. If the joint comes over a frame, it is usually possible to use screws (fig. 13 G).

If the butt joint is made in position it is possible to merely arrange it under the first panel and between lengthwise members (fig. 13 H). Mark a centre-line on the strap and fix it with glue and nails or screws. Scrape away the glue from the exposed part of the strap. When the second panel is fitted, use plenty of glue and push the new piece well up against the first so that the glue oozes up the joint. When this is sanded later the meeting line should be inconspicuous.

Wood has to be bent in building any boat. In larger craft quite stout wood is made flexible by steaming. The wood is put in some sort of a case, into which steam is admitted. The effect is to make the wood very pliable so that it can be bent more and easier than when it is dry. However, in most modern small boats, including all mentioned in this book, steaming is unnecessary.

The wood specified for a part can be expected to bend as much as necessary. Wood, being a natural product, varies and sometimes a piece may have flaws or be affected in some way that makes bending difficult, but usually bending needs no special treatment. It is good policy to prebend parts which you know will have to be pulled to shape. Strips can be sprung to a curve several days before they are actually needed. How this is done depends on their length and size, but strips can be jammed under a doorway or a bench. The actual curve need not be the final one.

If a piece is stubborn, it is always best to try bending the sharpest curve first. An awkward chine piece is more likely to take a curve if it is attached to the stem first and pulled back (fig. 13 I) than if that end is left last. If it is sprung around and you feel that pulling it down completely will crack it, it may be left overnight partly bent and tied (fig. 13 J). Next day it will probably go. If you have doubts about a particular piece of wood bending dry it may be wrapped with cloth soaked in hot water. This is also effective on plywood, although the glue prevents the water penetrating farther than the outside ply. A snag with using water is that glue cannot be used on damp wood, and after wetting to bend, the piece must be allowed to dry out before finally gluing and screwing in place. Sometimes drilling a stressed piece of wood may cause it to break. In that case it is permissible to rely only on the glue.

One way of bending a really stubborn piece of wood, or of getting it around a curve which would normally be too small in any case, is to slit the wood with a fine saw to a point past where the curve is to be (fig. 13 K). Spring this cut open and fill the slot with glue, then pull the part to shape (fig. 13 L). The two parts will slide over each other and take the shape, but when the glue has set they will be at least as strong as solid wood.

In boat building surfaces often have to be "faired off". When a plywood panel is to be fitted to framing, obviously the parts of the framing which come against the panel should be level, otherwise projections may prevent the panel fitting down, or hollows may make weak points where the parts do not touch. Fairing off is the preparation of the framework.

The need to fair off should be kept in mind when assembling the framework. It is easier to level off the comparatively narrow edge of a frame than the whole length of a projecting stringer, so if lengthwise parts are not exactly level, they are better slightly below than above a notch in a frame. Where a gunwale or chine goes through a frame at an angle, the notch should be deep enough to allow of fairing off the frame to the lengthwise part (fig. 14 A) rather than having to take some off the long piece.

Fairing off is checked by using rules and straight-edges. In many places the skin will be flat, but where it is twisted the testing must allow for the curves (fig. 14 B).

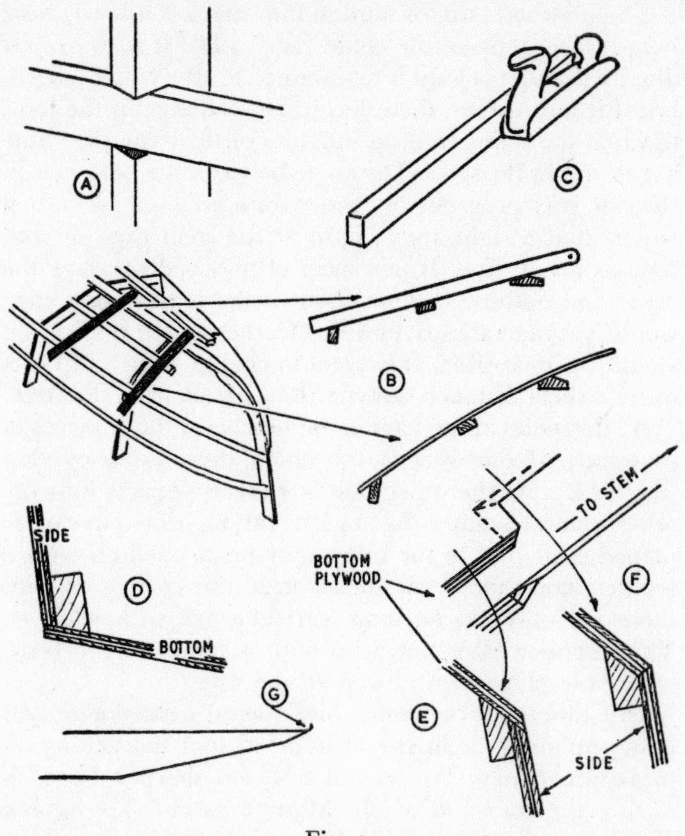

Fig. 14

The levelling may be done with a plane. Where several parts meet and grains are in different directions a disc sander on an electric drill is useful, but be careful of taking too much off. A shaping tool, of the Surform type is good for this work. Both plane and Surform tool can be improved for fairing off if they are extended by wood (fig. 14 C). When working on one surface, the extension on the tool maintains the correct angle by rubbing on another surface.

The plywood skin for most of the length of a hard chine boat merely laps on the chine (fig. 14 D). If it is a pram dinghy this sort of joint is maintained for the whole length, but if it has a stem, there has to be a change in the joint towards the stem. In most dinghies of this type the chine sweeps up to the stem. The angle between the bottom and the side goes progressively wider from an angle not much wider than a right-angle, until at the stem the side and bottom are in line. If one sheet of plywood overlaps the other and nothing is done about it the overlapping edge would get increasingly fine and feather-edged until a lap would be impossible. It is usual to change from a lap to a mitre a short distance (maybe 18 in.) back from the stem.

At this point there have to be notches in both pieces of plywood. At one side of the notch there is an overlap (fig. 14 E). At the other side one piece projects into the other to form a mitre (fig. 14 F). Although the lap can be planed, and part of the mitre may be cleaned off with a rebate plane, for a few inches near the change of joint there will have to be some careful work with a chisel. This problem does not arise with a double-chine boat, where the plywood is mitred all the way.

One difference between a professional woodworker and many amateurs is in the attitude to tool sharpening. A professional may stop several times to sharpen his tools during the course of a job. Many amateurs keep going with blunt tools and regarded sharpening as something of a special occasion, instead of an incidental job to be tackled many times a day. Planes, in particular, cannot produce a good surface when blunt and the effort needed to use them increases considerably. Saw sharpening may be left to the expert, although touching up saw teeth is not very difficult if the hints in the sawmaker's booklet are followed.

To sharpen edge tools an oilstone about 6 in. × 2 in. is needed. One made from a medium grit will do, although it is possible to get a double-sided one, having a coarse

8. Pete is light enough to be carried easily.

9. Pete: fixing a side. Note the strut holding the bottom in shape.

10. Pete: keel and rubbing strips fixed to the bottom.

11. Pete: fitting bottom boards as the boat nears completion.

side for quickly rubbing down a bad edge, such as removing the notch caused by hitting a screw. Use a thin oil with the stone. The thinnest lubricating oil, or even paraffin, is better than a thick oil, which clogs the stone and prevents the grit getting at the steel. Always wipe a stone clean and protect it from dirt when out of use.

The existing bevel on a plane iron or chisel will give you a clue to the angle to hold the tool on the stone. Rub it at this angle for the greater part of the length of the stone. A fault to overcome is the tendency to dip your hands towards the far end of the stone, causing a rounded edge on the blade. One hand should hold the handle of the chisel or the top of the plane iron. This hand maintains the angle. The other hand provides pressure, with the fingers spread out if it is a wide blade (photo 4).

Continue rubbing at this angle until a wire edge can be felt—when you run a finger down the flat side and over the edge a roughness can be felt. This indicates that the bevel has been rubbed down to a sharp edge and a particle of the steel sharpened off is still clinging to it (fig. 14 G). Remove this wire edge, first by rubbing the flat side absolutely flat on the stone (photo 5), then by slicing across a piece of scrap wood.

Varnish and paint are not difficult to apply, but poor work here can spoil the appearance of what is otherwise good workmanship. A new tin of varnish can be used straight away without stirring—in fact stirring should be avoided as this causes air bubbles which will dry out as little circles on the work. A partly-used tin may be found to have a skin on it. This should be removed and discarded, otherwise bits of skin will spoil the surface. Most paints need stirring before use. The thick paste in the bottom should be well worked into the liquid. Some synthetic paints are less troublesome than the older types. Paint skin should also be removed.

Paint should be applied by laying off in several directions before finally brushing in the same direction—

usually lengthwise. As painting progresses, hard lines can be avoided if the final brush strokes are taken back towards the previous part and the brush lifted as it passes over the earlier part. Spread the paint well. If it is very thick, it may not be possible to work it out thoroughly and it will dry either with brush marks or with "runs" on vertical surfaces. Thinners may be used to improve the spread of the paint, but only a very small amount needs to be added.

Varnish needs less vigorous brushing than paint, otherwise air bubbles will form and mar the surface. Modern varnishes can be used in conditions where traditional types made from natural lacs would be troublesome, but the modern synthetic varnishes will give a better finish if used in the right conditions. The varnish may be warmed slightly. Working conditions should be fairly warm. Dust is the enemy of varnish, so a sheltered warm place is best. If you are working outdoors and the boat is to stay outdoors, get the varnish on before noon so that it is almost hard before nightfall and cannot be affected by dew or the cool of night.

If you use a polyurethane finish, get the maker's instruction book and follow it exactly. These expensive paints and varnishes have to be applied correctly, otherwise they are wasted.

Paint and varnish brushes are best cleaned with one of the proprietary brush cleaners and stored dry for the next occasion. They may be kept wet between coats and for short periods, but long storage in liquid is not a good thing, under the usual amateur conditions. Putting the brush in water prevents evaporation of the paint in the bristles. If the water is removed by working out the brush on some scrap wood, it will then be ready for use. Varnish brushes may be kept for a short period in thinners.

Chapter 6

PETE—6 FT. PRAM DINGHY

A PRAM dinghy is simple to build, because there are no great curves or twists as there may be when a short boat is built with a stem. It also gives a greater carrying capacity than a similarly-proportioned boat of the same length with a stem. The boat may also be lighter, and is usually more economical to build. The simplest pram has a flat bottom, which is quite satisfactory for use in inland waters or the conditions usually found in harbours. A flat bottom is convenient for dragging over mud, and it has the minimum draught so it can be taken into places too shallow for other boats.

Pete (fig. 15) (photos 6, 7, 8) is designed as the smallest practicable pram dinghy. It is light enough for a child to carry. It will ferry two adults or can be used as a play boat for two or three children. The angler will find it useful, as he can carry it to the water unaided. It is no trouble on the roof of a car, and might even be pushed into the boot of some cars. Simple sailing gear can be added, but too much must not be expected from it. A flat-bottomed boat cannot sail very well and class racing dinghy performance must not be expected, but with the rig described Pete can provide a lot of fun for single-handed sailing. All of the sailing gear will stow inside the boat when not in use.

Building is very economical. If there is a joint in one side, all of the skin may be cut from one sheet of plywood. A little more plywood is needed if a joint is to be avoided. At the time of writing this boat can be built with a plywood skin in Britain for a little over £4 and with a tempered hardboard skin for rather less. This is the cheapest

PETE

6 FT. PRAM DINGHY

Material Schedule

All solid wood parts may be made from any straight-grained softwood or hardwood. All plywood parts should be marine grade. Widths and thicknesses of solid wood are finished sizes, but lengths are full. Sizes of plywood parts allow a little for shaping.

Part	*Number required*	*Length in.*	*Width in.*	*Thickness in.*
Transom	1	33	$15\frac{1}{2}$	$\frac{3}{4}$ solid or plywood
	1	33	$15\frac{1}{2}$	$\frac{3}{16}$ or 4 mm. plywood
or	1	26	$1\frac{1}{2}$	$\frac{3}{4}$
	2	15	$1\frac{1}{2}$	$\frac{3}{4}$
	1	33	4	$\frac{3}{4}$
Bow board	1	18	9	$\frac{3}{4}$ solid or plywood
	1	18	9	$\frac{3}{16}$ or 4 mm. plywood
or	1	15	$1\frac{1}{2}$	$\frac{3}{4}$
	2	9	$1\frac{1}{2}$	$\frac{3}{4}$
	1	18	3	$\frac{3}{4}$
Chines	2	72	$\frac{3}{4}$	$\frac{3}{4}$
Gunwales	2	76	$\frac{3}{4}$	$\frac{3}{4}$
Bottom stiffeners	1	36	4	$\frac{3}{4}$
Bottom stiffeners	2	32	$1\frac{1}{2}$	$\frac{3}{4}$
Thwart	1	38	6	$\frac{3}{4}$
Thwart supports	2	12	6	$\frac{3}{4}$
Rowlock swells	2	5	$1\frac{1}{2}$	$\frac{3}{4}$
Rowlock swells	2	5	$2\frac{1}{4}$	$\frac{1}{2}$
Thole pins	4	6	$\frac{1}{2}$	round, optional, ash
Knees, from	1	30	3	$\frac{3}{4}$
Keel	1	66	2	$\frac{3}{4}$
Bottom rubbers	2	66	$\frac{3}{4}$	$\frac{3}{4}$
Gunwale rubbers	2	76	$1\frac{1}{2}$	$\frac{1}{2}$
Chine rubbers	2	72	$1\frac{1}{2}$	$\frac{1}{2}$

Bottom boards	8	30	4	$\frac{3}{8}$
Bottom boards	2	30	6	$\frac{3}{8}$
Bottom boards	2	22	6	$\frac{3}{8}$
(or equivalent in narrow boards of plywood offcuts)				
Bottom boards	4	36	$1\frac{1}{2}$	$\frac{3}{4}$
Bottom boards	2	30	$1\frac{1}{2}$	$\frac{3}{4}$
Skin	1	96	48	$\frac{3}{16}$ or 4 mm. plywood
or				
	1	96	48	$\frac{1}{8}$ oil-tempered hardboard
Sailing Gear				
Mast	1	69	$2\frac{1}{2}$	$2\frac{1}{2}$
Spars	2	69	$1\frac{1}{4}$	$1\frac{1}{4}$
Leeboard	1	30	6	$\frac{1}{2}$ plywood
Mast thwart	1	24	5	$\frac{3}{4}$
Rudder, from	1	28	12	$\frac{3}{8}$ plywood
Tiller	1	24	$\frac{7}{8}$	$\frac{7}{8}$ preferably ash

Sundries (approximate quantities)

8 doz. $\frac{3}{4}$ in × 5 or 6 gauge countersunk brass screws (plywood skin).

or

8 doz. $\frac{5}{8}$ in. × 4 gauge countersunk brass screws (hardboard skin).

2 doz. $1\frac{1}{4}$ in. × 6 gauge countersunk brass screws (framework).
(or annular ring nails, see page 50).

$\frac{1}{4}$ lb. $\frac{3}{4}$ in. thin brass nails (skin).

$\frac{1}{4}$ lb. $1\frac{1}{2}$ in. galvanized or copper nails (framework).

1 pair 2 in. galvanized rowlocks and plates (optional).

1 set gudgeons and pintles, or stout screw eyes and rod (rudder).

1 $1\frac{1}{2}$ in. × $\frac{1}{4}$ in. brass bolt with washer and wing nut (rudder).

2 3 in. metal cleats (mast), or make wooden ones.

About 24 ft. hemp or sisal rope $1\frac{1}{4}$ in. circumference ($\frac{3}{8}$ in. diameter).

$\frac{1}{2}$ lb. synthetic resin glue.

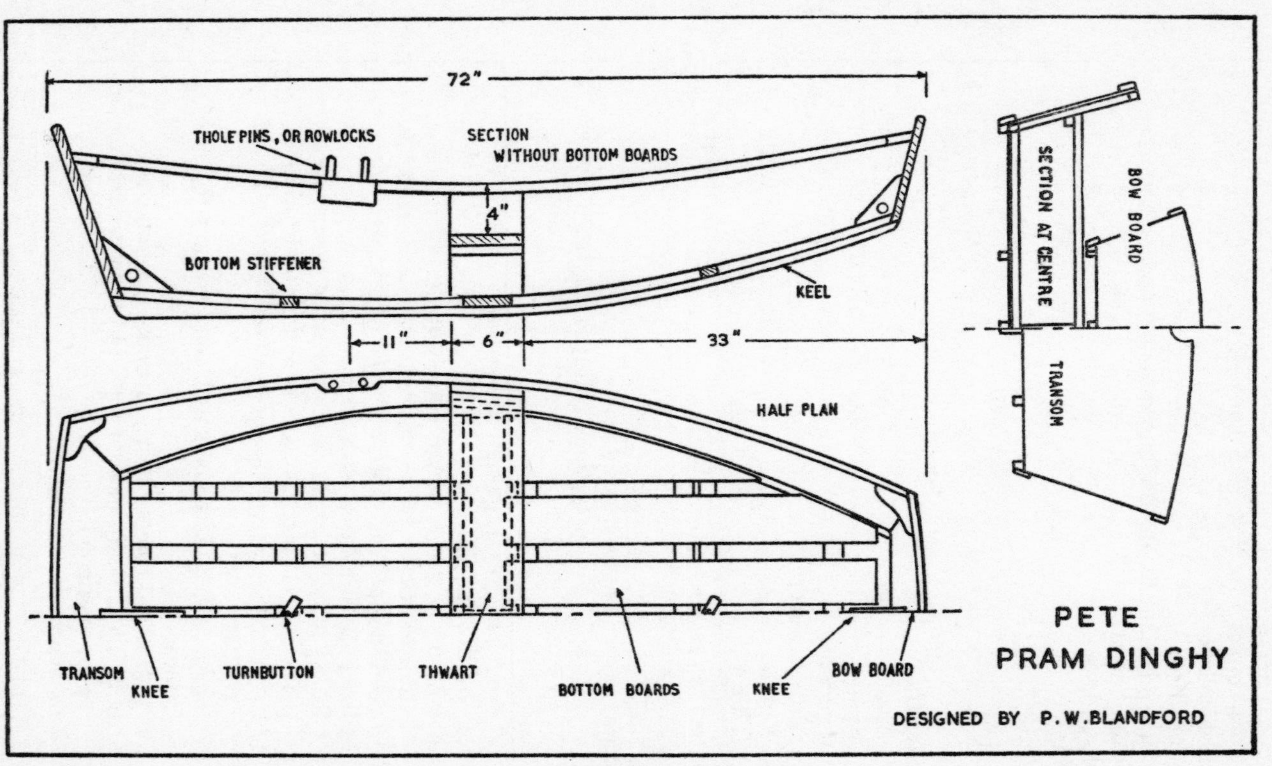
72"
THOLE PINS, OR ROWLOCKS
SECTION
WITHOUT BOTTOM BOARDS
4"
BOTTOM STIFFENER
KEEL
11"
6"
33"
HALF PLAN
TRANSOM
KNEE
TURNBUTTON
THWART
BOTTOM BOARDS
KNEE
BOW BOARD
SECTION AT CENTRE
BOW BOARD
TRANSOM
PETE
PRAM DINGHY
DESIGNED BY P. W. BLANDFORD

Fig. 15

boat that can be built—cheaper even than a small fabric-covered canoe.

The wood needed is listed in the material schedule, but variations are possible without seriously affecting the boat. The original boat, which is still sound after five years use, has a skin made from oil-tempered hardboard, with the other timber cut from a dismantled old wardrobe. Plywood makes a stronger skin. Its thickness depends on the strength required. A carefully-used dinghy may have 4 mm. plywood and be extremely light, but increasing to 5 or 6 mm. makes a much stronger job. The transom and bow board may be made of solid wood or they can be built up by framing plywood. If an outboard motor is to be used, the transom should be solid, or the top 6 in. backed with solid wood if it is made of plywood.

Start by making the bottom. Draw a line 18 in. from one edge of the plywood sheet and draw lines across it (fig. 16 A). Alternatively, use a full-size drawing (see Preface). Mark the widths on these lines and use a batten bent through the points to draw the curves, then cut out the bottom, using a fine hand saw or a tenon saw.

Make the transom and bow board (fig. 17 A, B). Bevel the edges to the angles indicated. Although the top edges will be rounded later, it is advisable to leave them square across at this stage so that knocks are only likely to damage wood which will later be cleaned off. A sculling notch is useful in the transom, both for sculling in narrow waters and for serving the angler as a rod rest (fig. 17 C). This may be cut with a coping saw.

Make the knees (fig. 17 D). Fix them with glue and screws to the transom and bow board, then fix these assemblies to the ends of the bottom. If hardboard is used, have the smooth side downwards. Use glue and screws at about 3 in. intervals. See that both end boards are at right-angles to the centre-line of the bottom.

Make the chine pieces. Plane the strips to the angle shown (fig. 17 E). This is approximate and will probably

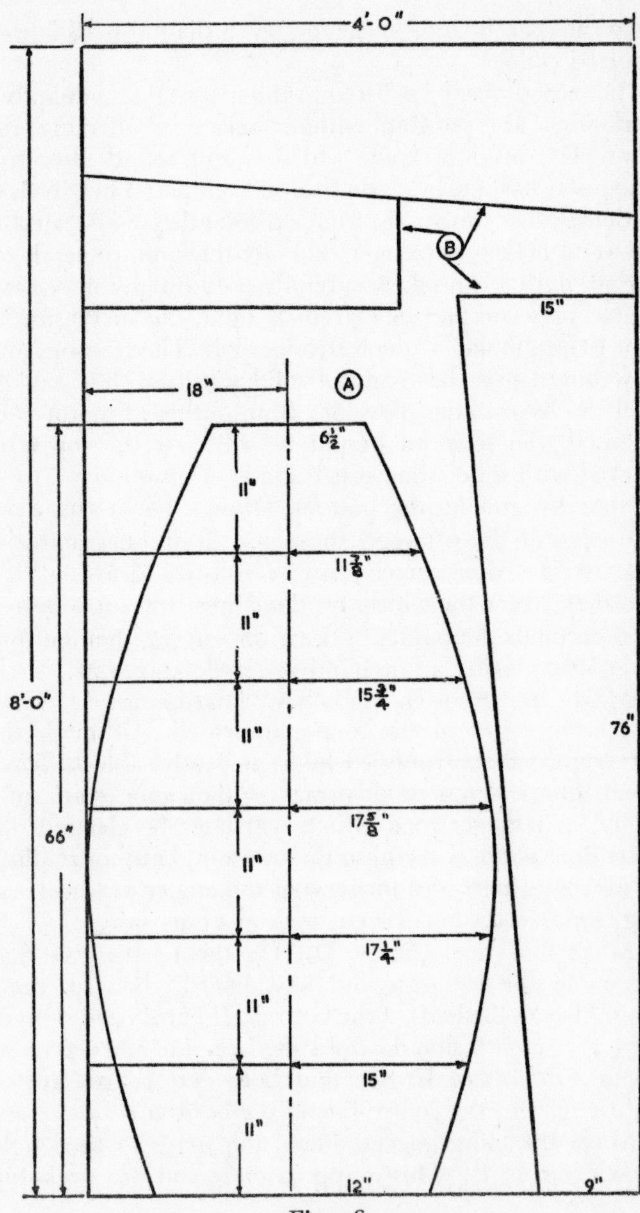

Fig. 16

need little change at the centre of the boat, but the bevel will have to be modified after fixing, when the surfaces are faired off towards the ends. Cut the chines so that they will spring to shape between the ends. Glue them in place and hold with cramps while screws are driven from below. For economy, screws may be at about 9 in. intervals and brass nails may be driven intermediately to finish at about 3 in. intervals. Make and fit the three crosswise bottom stiffeners (fig. 18 A). They should be securely glued, and nailed or screwed from outside. Let the glue set before doing any more work on the assembly. Plane the bottom edges flush with the chines.

Make the two side panels (fig. 16 B). Top and bottom edges are straight. If one side is to be made in two parts, have one piece 4 ft. long, cut across a sheet, and another to make up the length. Use the one-piece side to mark out these parts. Have a piece of similar material to make the butt strap or joint cover (fig. 17 F). Cut it back to allow for the thicknesses of the gunwale and chine. Make the joint, using glue and $\frac{3}{4}$ in. nails driven through and clenched inside. Let this joint set before shaping the side.

Support the boat on two boxes or blocks in a position where a strut can be used to apply pressure from above. A doorway is a suitable place. The pressure needed is not excessive, but the place used should be firm. Use any convenient strip of wood to force the bottom to a curve about 3 in. deep (fig. 18 B). Try one side in position, with its top edge level with bow board and transom. Experiment with the amount of curve in the bottom. You should find a point where the flare of the side combined with the curve allows the straight edge of the side to conform closely to the chine. If this cannot be obtained exactly, mark the final shape on the lower edge of the side. Cut it to this and shape the other side to match.

With a side in position, note what alteration may be needed to the angles of chine or either end board. Fair

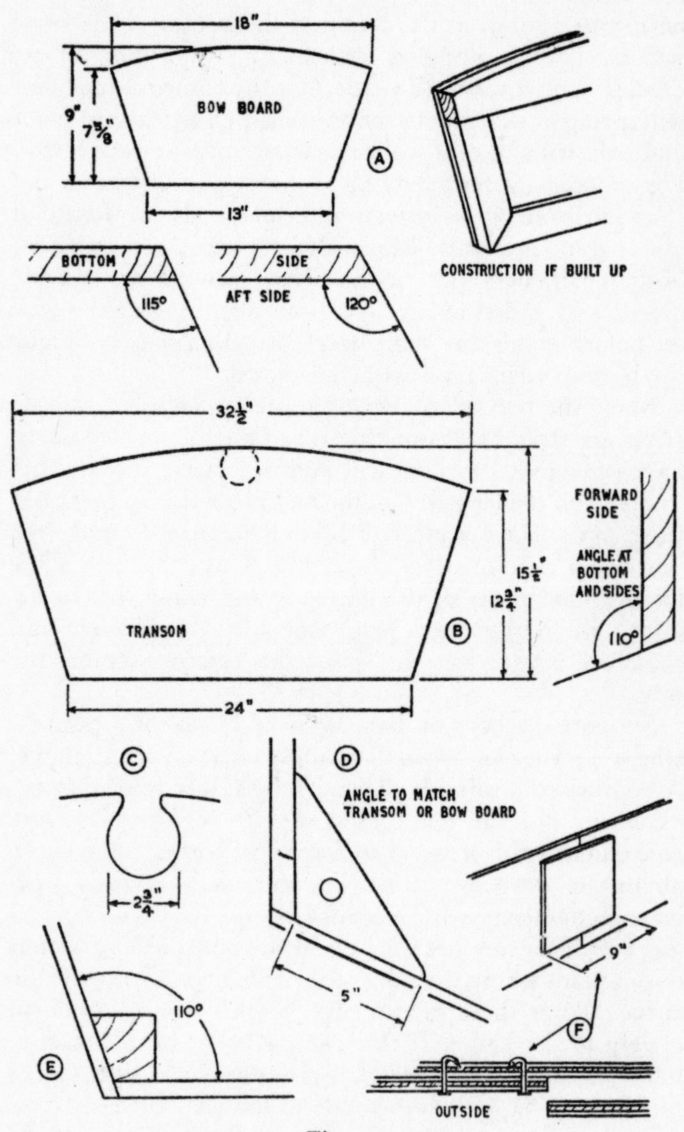
18"
9"
7 5/8"
BOW BOARD
A
13"
CONSTRUCTION IF BUILT UP
BOTTOM
SIDE
AFT SIDE
115°
120°
32 1/2"
FORWARD SIDE
15 1/2"
12 3/4"
ANGLE AT BOTTOM AND SIDES
TRANSOM
B
110°
24"
C
D
ANGLE TO MATCH TRANSOM OR BOW BOARD
2 3/4"
9"
110°
5"
F
E
OUTSIDE

Fig. 17

these off and try again. It may be necessary to fair and test several times before a reasonably close joint is obtained. If much alteration to an angle is made at one side, check with an adjustable bevel that the angle at the opposite side is made the same.

Sight from one end to see that the assembly is not twisted—a view of one end board over the other will show if there is any distortion. Put one side in position and mark on it where other parts will come. Cut off most of the surplus at the ends. Drill for screws at about 9 in. intervals. Glue and screw them into position (photo 9). Fix both sides, with nails at about 3 in. intervals along the chines and additional screws in the end posts.

Fix the gunwales in the same way (fig. 18 C). At the thwart position fix strips of the same material as the thwart between the chines and gunwales, with bearers to support the twart (fig. 18 D). To prevent the sides springing, nail a scrap strip of wood across the gunwales near the centre, then knock out the strut from the roof. Make the thwart and fix it to the supports at each side, and put a short support under the centre of the thwart, then remove the scrap piece of wood across the gunwales. Thicken the gunwales at the rowing position (fig. 18 E). Either drill for metal rowlocks and their plates, or fix two pieces of dowel rod to act as thole pins.

From this stage the boat may be moved around and put in any convenient position for working. Clean off any projecting edges, but do not round any of them until all the other parts are fitted. Fit knees at all four corners (fig. 18 F). Glue them and screw from outside. Round the inner edges well. These knees are often the places used for lifting.

Fit a stout gunwale rubbing strip. This provides strength as well as taking rubs and knocks (fig. 18 G). With a plywood bottom it should be sufficient to put a similar rubbing strip at each side around the chine (fig. 18 H), but with a hardboard bottom some additional protection may

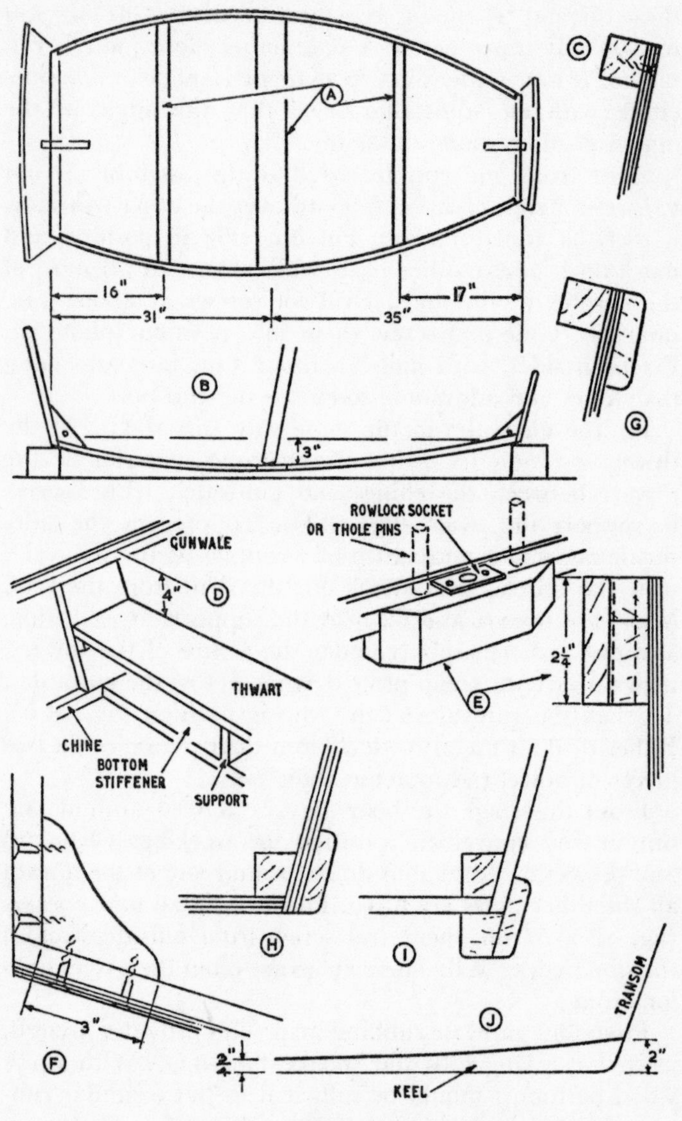

A
B
C
16"
17"
31"
35"
3"
G
ROWLOCK SOCKET
OR THOLE PINS
GUNWALE
4"
D
THWART
CHINE
BOTTOM
STIFFENER
SUPPORT
E
2¼"
F
3"
H
I
J
TRANSOM
2"
KEEL

Fig. 18

be provided by a strip bent around underneath before the side rubbing strip is fitted (fig. 18 I).

A central outside keel helps to keep the boat straight as well as provide protection. This may be a piece of $\frac{3}{4}$ in. square strip throughout the length, but it is better to use a piece about 2 in. deep and taper it in the length so as to form a skeg aft (fig. 18 J). Two other strips parallel to it stiffen the bottom and provide additional protection (photo 10). All of these parts are fixed with glue and screws driven at about 6 in. intervals from inside the boat.

It is important that the skin is not walked on, and it is best to fit all-over bottom boards (photo 11), so that the load of any local pressure is spread by them. Those shown are made up in two parts, resting on the stiffening cross-pieces and held down by blocks and turnbuttons. It is possible to use offcuts of plywood for bottom boards, or they can be made of any softwood strips (fig. 19 A). The turnbuttons may be wood or metal.

Clean up all the woodwork. Remove any surplus glue. If hardboard is used, avoid breaking the hard surface of the smooth side with tools or glasspaper. Thoroughly paint or varnish all over, with a total of at least three coats.

If the boat is to be used for rowing or for using with an outboard motor it is finished. Oars need only be about 5 ft. long. Instructions for making them are given in Chapter 11. Fix a rope for use as a painter through the hole in the bow knee. If the dinghy is to be towed behind another boat it will be better to fix a ring bolt through the bow board, within an inch or so of the bottom, with the ring outside, so that the towing rope lifts the bow.

Only the simplest sailing gear is worth having on such a small boat. There is really insufficient room for a dagger board, although it would not be impossible to fit one forward of the thwart. Instead, a leeboard is shown. By using this the boat does not have to be altered. A single board is used, held by a rope to a screw eye in the bottom. When you go about you transfer the board to

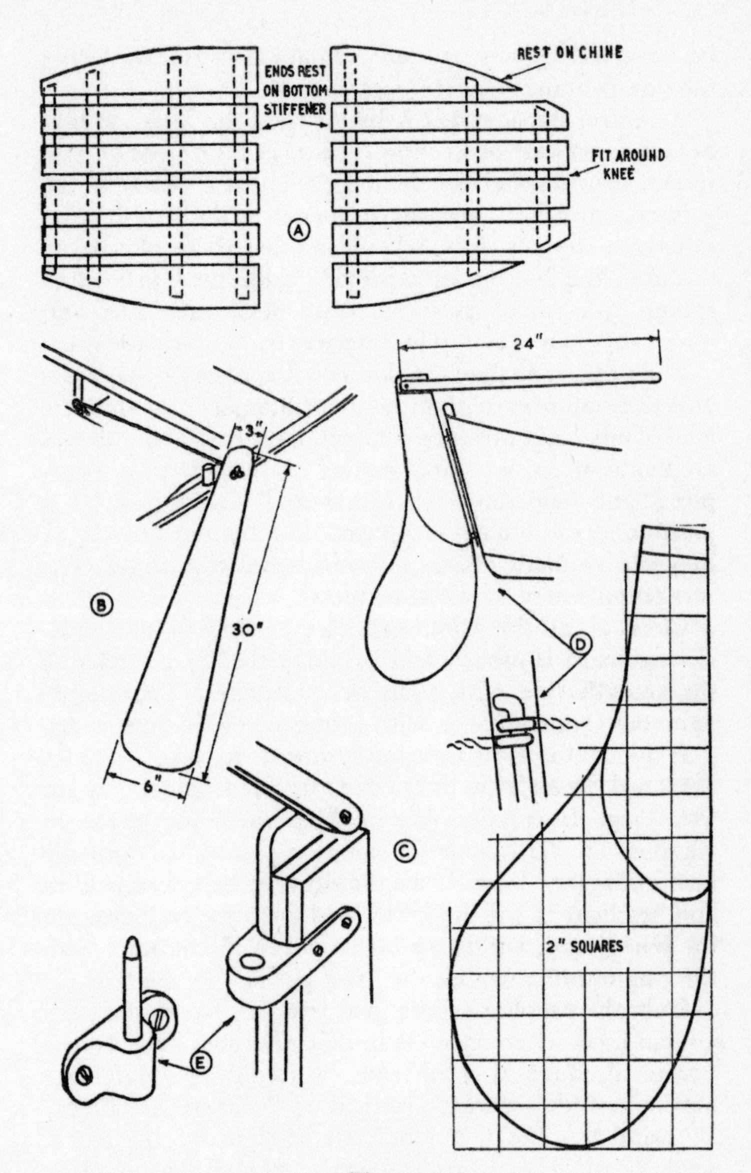
ENDS REST
ON BOTTOM
STIFFENER
REST ON CHINE
FIT AROUND
KNEE
A
24"
3"
30"
6"
B
D
C
2" SQUARES
E

Fig. 19

the other side. It should be on the lee side (the side away from the wind), with the rope against a thole pin or a peg pushed in the rowlock socket. Make the board from $\frac{3}{8}$ in. plywood and well round its edges (fig. 19 B).

The rudder stock and blade are all $\frac{3}{8}$ in. plywood. In a little dinghy it is convenient to be able to hinge the tiller upwards, so this one is pivoted on one side of the stock (fig. 19 C). The tiller is best made of ash, but any hardwood may be used. The simplest rudder hangings are made from screw eyes, with a rod dropped through (fig. 19 D). Alternatively, use proper gudgeons and pintles (fig. 19 E).

The mast and both spars (fig. 20 A) are best made of spruce, but any straight-grained softwood may be used. See that the wood is straight. The yard and boom are parallel, but the mast should be planed to a square taper before rounding. Round the wood in stages. Reduce it first to a regular octagon. This may be done by eye, but if diagonals are drawn on the end and half the length of one of them measured, that will be the distance from the edge of the square to the corner of the octagon (fig. 20 B). Plane the corners off the octagon, then remove any sharp angles and round the wood with strips of glasspaper used across the grain (fig. 20 C).

The mast is supported by a thwart across the gunwales and a slotted block on the bottom boards or the centre of the hull (fig. 20 D). The mast should be upright when the boat is afloat. The halliard may pass through a hole near the top of the mast or there can be a small pulley, or sheave, let into a slot. Round the ends of the other spars and drill a hole near each end.

The sail is made from a light grade of sailcloth, or any closely-woven fabric. Any seams may be parallel to the foot or the leech. Turn in a tabling all round and on all edges except the leech sew on tape (fig. 20 E). At the corners fix eyelets through reinforcing triangles and put other eyelets at about 12 in. intervals along head and

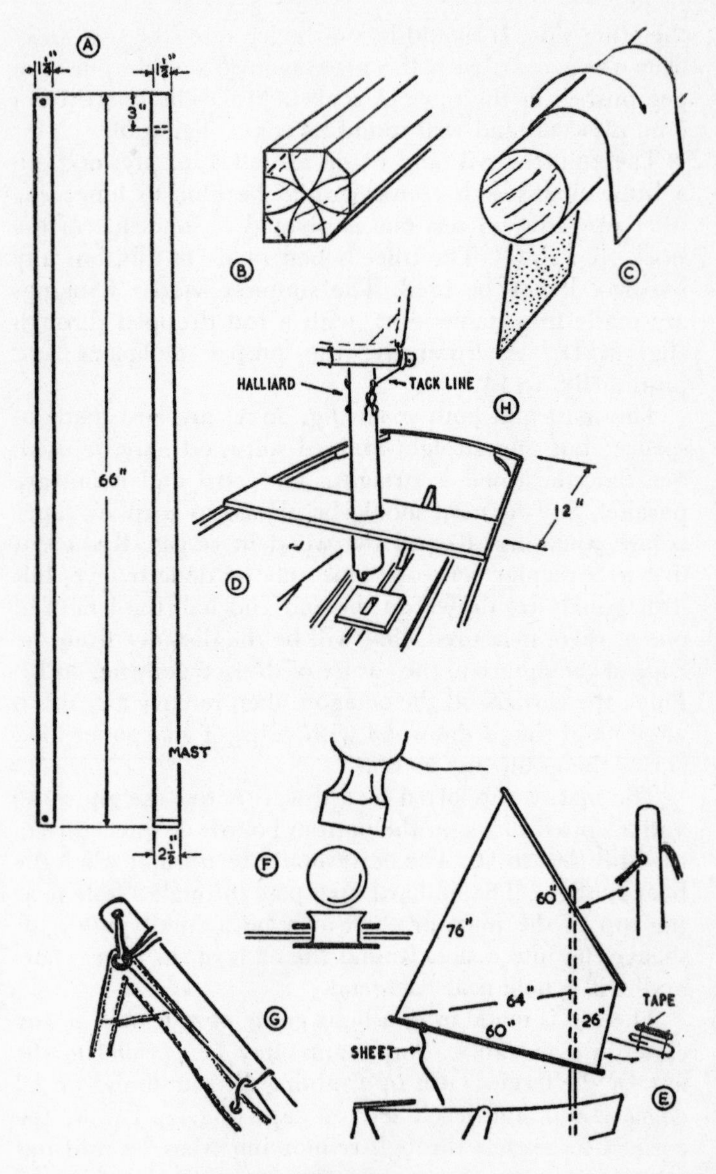
A
1¼"
1½"
3"
66"
MAST
2½"
B
C
HALLIARD
TACK LINE
H
12"
D
F
G
60"
76"
64"
26"
60"
TAPE
SHEET
E

Fig. 20

12. Corrib.

13. Corrib: fixing a chine to frame 1.

14. Corrib: the framework completed and being faired off to take the skin.

15. Corrib: fixing a bottom panel. A screw is being driven into the chine just aft of the change in skin joint.

foot. If special closing tools are unavailable, eyelets may be fixed in the following way. Use a spike to make a hole. This is better than punching a hole as the pushed up cloth will become trapped in the eyelet and help to secure it. Push the eyelet through then slip its ring on the other side, then start spreading the middle with a centre punch, followed by a steel ball (fig. 20 F) and a final flattening with a hammer.

Fasten the corner eyelets to the holes in the ends of the spars, then lace along the spars with half hitches (fig. 20 G). Tie the halliard to the yard and make a trial hoist. Arrange the position of this knot so that the boom can be pulled back to the mast with a short tack line and it will slope upwards towards the stern (fig. 20 H). Fasten about 8 ft. of line to the boom to act as a sheet. Fix a cleat on one side of the mast for the tack line and one at the other side for the halliard.

After a trial assembly, dismantle the gear and varnish the mast and spars, and paint the leeboard and rudder to match the rest of the boat.

SBS F

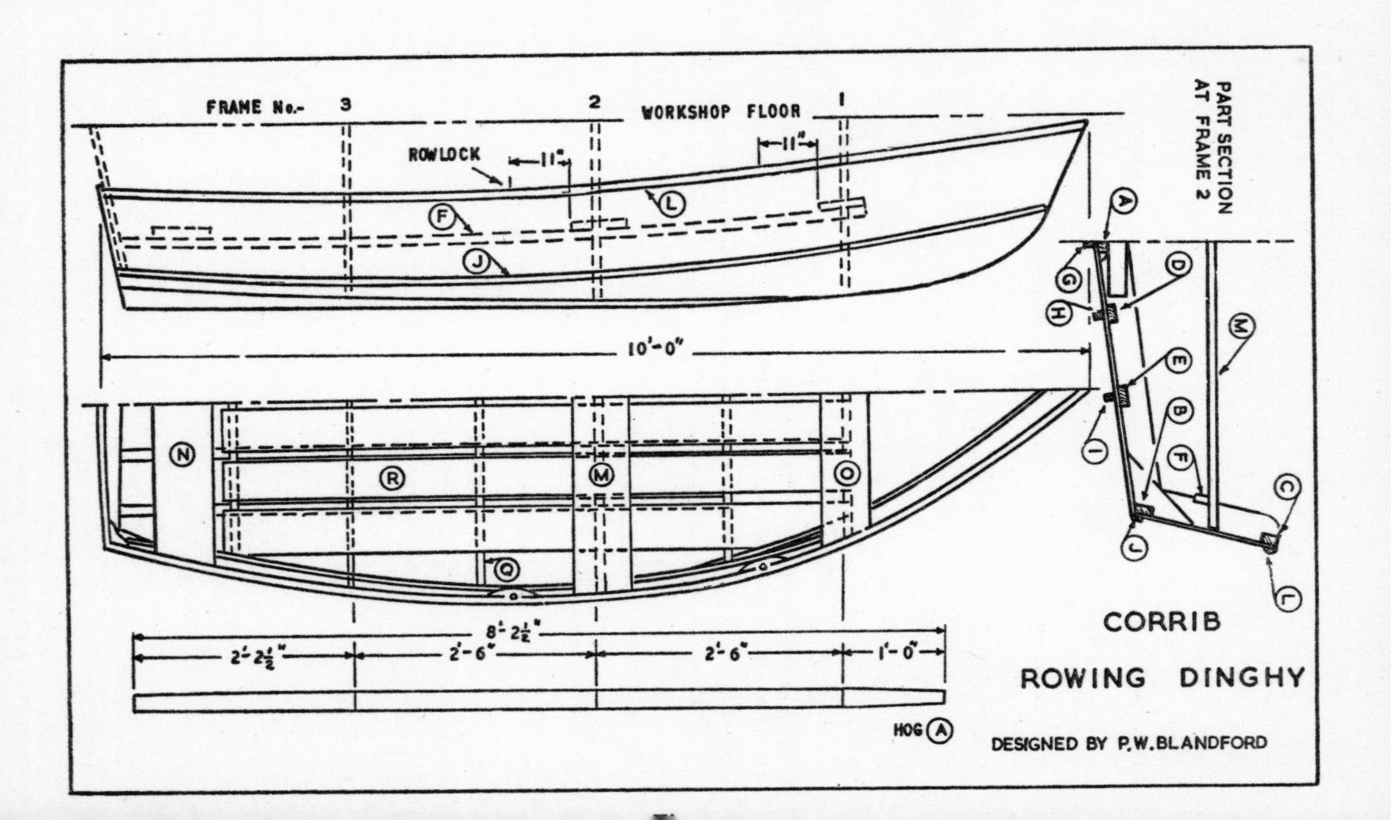
FRAME No.- 3 2 1
WORKSHOP FLOOR
ROWLOCK
11"
11"
L
F
J
10'-0"
PART SECTION
AT FRAME 2
A
G
H
D
E
I
B
F
M
C
J
L
N
R
M
O
Q
8'-2½"
2'-2½"
2'-6"
2'-6"
1'-0"
HOG A
CORRIB
ROWING DINGHY
DESIGNED BY P.W.BLANDFORD

Chapter 7

CORRIB—10 FT. HARD-CHINE STEM DINGHY

At one time most owners of yachts used a clinker-built dinghy of about 10 ft. length as a tender, and this became accepted as the general-purpose boat for anyone wanting a craft for rowing or outboard use, on tidal or inland waters, whether they had a larger boat or not. That was before the days of marine plywood and when craftsmen skilled in clinker boat building were plentiful and wages much lower. To-day boats built in this traditional way are expensive to buy and too difficult for most amateurs to build. Corrib (fig. 21) is designed as a general-purpose boat, built in modern materials to take advantage of their properties and particularly in simplicity of building. This is a boat for all sorts of jobs. It will ferry people to an anchored yacht, it will take a party of three for a picnic up the river (photo 12), the angler will find it easy to manage and roomy for his purpose, the single-hander will find that it is not too big to manage alone, and it can be regarded as a maid of all work. It can be sculled over the stern, or a small outboard motor (about 1½ h.p.) can be cramped on to give a satisfactory speed. It is easily carried by two boys and will travel on the roof of a medium-sized car. It is the largest boat that can be got into the luggage van of most British trains.

The boat is built upside-down on frames which are extended to be fixed to the floor. This is the method used for building the majority of plywood-skinned boats. Anyone intending to build one of the large number of class sailing dinghies will find that in nearly all cases the method and sequence of building will be the same as described in this chapter.

CORRIB

10 FT. HARD-CHINE STEM DINGHY

Material Schedule

Frames are numbered. Main structural parts are lettered. All plywood should be of marine quality—in Great Britain marked BSS 1088. Many woods may be used for building this boat. It would look smartest if built completely in mahogany, but other woods are cheaper and in some cases have properties more suitable to the part's particular function. Suggested woods are:

S	Sitka spruce or yellow cedar	P	Parana pine
D	Red deal	O	Oak or aframosia
M	Mahogany	A	Ash or rock elm

Part	*Name*	*Number required*	*Length ft.*	*in.*	*Width in.*	*Thickness in.*	*Wood*
	Stem	1	2	6	7	$1\frac{1}{2}$	P
	Frame 1	2	1	7	$2\frac{3}{8}$	$\frac{5}{8}$	P
		2	1	5	$2\frac{3}{8}$	$\frac{5}{8}$	P
		2	1	0	$2\frac{3}{8}$	$\frac{5}{8}$	P
		1		11	$1\frac{3}{8}$	$\frac{5}{8}$	P
	Frame 2	2	1	9	$2\frac{3}{8}$	$\frac{5}{8}$	P
		2	2	0	$2\frac{3}{8}$	$\frac{5}{8}$	P
		2		9	$2\frac{3}{8}$	$\frac{5}{8}$	P
		3		11	$1\frac{3}{8}$	$\frac{5}{8}$	P
	Frame 3	2	1	9	$2\frac{3}{8}$	$\frac{5}{8}$	P
		2	1	10	$2\frac{3}{8}$	$\frac{5}{8}$	P
		2		9	$2\frac{3}{8}$	$\frac{5}{8}$	P
		6		7	$1\frac{3}{8}$	$\frac{5}{8}$	P
		1		11	$1\frac{3}{8}$	$\frac{5}{8}$	P
	Transom	1	3	0	15	$\frac{3}{8}$	plywood
		2	1	8	$2\frac{3}{8}$	$\frac{5}{8}$	P
		2	1	4	$2\frac{3}{8}$	$\frac{5}{8}$	P
		1	2	8	$2\frac{3}{8}$	$\frac{5}{8}$	P
		1	1	1	$2\frac{3}{8}$	$\frac{5}{8}$	P
	Temporary struts	4	4	6	2	1	D
A	Hog	1	8	3	2	$\frac{7}{8}$	M or S
B	Chines	2	11	0	$1\frac{3}{8}$	$\frac{5}{8}$	S
C	Gunwales	2	11	6	$1\frac{3}{8}$	$\frac{5}{8}$	S
D	Bottom stiffeners						
	inner	2	8	0	$1\frac{3}{8}$	$\frac{5}{8}$	S or D

E	Bottom stiffeners outer	2	7	0	1 3/8	5/8	S or D
F	Risers	2	8	0	1 3/8	5/8	S or M
G	Keel	1	8	3	1	1	O or P
H	Bottom rubbers inner	2	8	0	3/4	3/4	O or P
I	Bottom rubbers outer	2	7	0	3/4	3/4	O or P
J	Chine rubbers	2	11	0	1	1/2	O or P
K	Skeg	1	4	0	2	1	O or P
L	Gunwale rubbers	2	11	6	1	half-round	M
M	Main thwart	1	4	2	7	7/8	M or D
N	Stern sheets	1	3	0	7	7/8	M or D
O	Bow thwart	1	3	1	7	7/8	M or D
P	Stem band	1	3	0	1 1/8	1/4	A
Q	Bottom board bearers	6	2	0	1 3/4	5/8	P or D
R	Bottom boards from	6	6	6	5	5/8	D
–	Bottom boards from	4	6	0	1 3/8	5/8	D
–	Knees	3		6	2 3/8	5/8	O or P
–	Rowlock swells	4		6	1 3/8	5/8	M
–	Rowlock cleats	4		5	1 3/8	5/8	M
	Skin	2	8	0	4′ 0″	5 or 6 mm.	plywood
		1	6	0	1′ 4″	5 or 6 mm.	plywood

Sundries (approximate quantities)

2 dozen 2 in. × 8 gauge countersunk brass screws (keel, framing)

8 dozen 1 1/4 in. × 6 gauge countersunk brass screws (framing)

3 gross 5/8 in. × 4 gauge countersunk brass screws (skin).
(or annular ring nails, see page 50).

About 3 lb. synthetic resin glue.

1/4 lb. 1 in. copper boat nails (framing).

1/4 lb. brass shoe nails (skin).

1/4 lb. stopping.

2 qts. varnish or equivalent paint.

1 piece brass, 3 ft. × 1/2 in. halfround (stem).

2 pairs 2 in. rowlocks and plates.

All parts are joined with synthetic resin glue and either screws or nails. For a painted finish the screw heads may be flush with the skin. Although the skin is not very thick it is just possible to countersink the screw heads below the surface and cover them with stopping if it is desired to hide them when a varnished finish is preferred.

Draw the frames full-size (or obtain a full-size drawing, see Preface). It will be sufficient to draw only half of each frame if space is restricted and turn the frame over when it is assembled on it (fig. 22). Make the frames, transom and stem. Assemble the frames over the drawing. Glue and nail or screw the joint covers at the chines on the two halves of each frame, then check the overall width when assembling the joint between the pairs of parts. Make the slots of a suitable width to suit the actual wood which is to fit into them.

The edges of frame 2 may be left square, but the transom and other frames may be bevelled slightly, as shown, to avoid awkward planing later when fairing off. Thickening pieces, which form skin joint covers, may be fixed to the bottom of frame 3 and the sides of frame 2 now, or left until later.

The stem may be made from one piece of thick wood, or it may be built up from two or more cut to shape and glued up, if preferred. The forward edge should be given an approximate bevel, in readiness for fairing off later. The transom framing is glued and nailed to the plywood which forms the solid part. The extra piece at the centre provides stiffening for an outboard motor cramp. Round the upper edge as much as the framing permits. Inner edges of frames may also be rounded. Slots in the transom are in the framing only, and should not be taken through the plywood.

Mark out the floor (fig. 23, 1). It is simplest to set frame 2 square with the centre-line and make the other frame positions parallel to it. Nail or screw the temporary struts to the floor near their ends so that it will not be difficult to

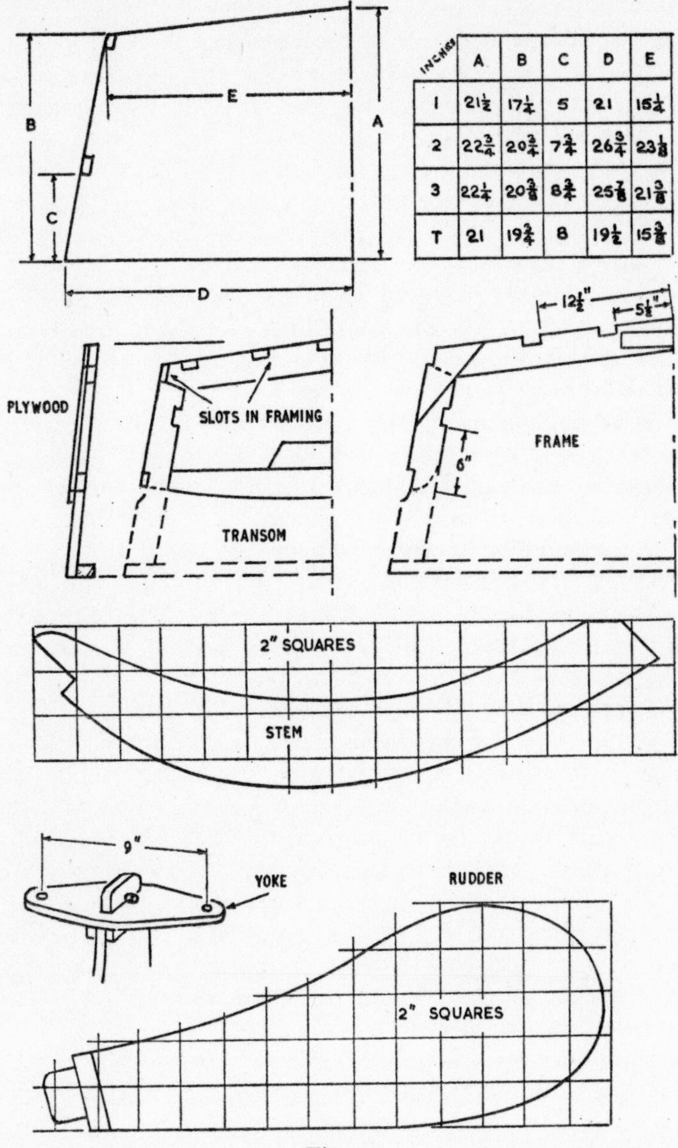

INCHES	A	B	C	D	E
1	21½	17¼	5	21	15¼
2	22¾	20¾	7¾	26¾	23⅛
3	22¼	20⅜	8¾	25⅞	21⅜
T	21	19¾	8	19½	15⅜

Fig. 22

withdraw the fastenings later. If there is any doubt about the stability of the floor or the fastenings to it, fix a stiff plank over the temporary struts and alongside the stem.

Make the hog (A) (fig. 21). Mark a centre-line along its underside. Taper in width from frame 1 to the stem recess. With the centre-line as a guide, give the underside a preliminary bevel, using the frames as a guide to the angles. Fix the hog to the frames and stem. Pull the transom in to suit. Check that the assembly is straight by sighting along it. Fix the two pairs of bottom stiffeners (D and E) (fig. 21 and 24, 1). The inner ones (D) should be about 2 in. through frame 1. The outer ones (E) should extend to about halfway between frames 1 and 2.

Bend a gunwale (C) temporarily into place, cramp it in position at each frame and allow it to project over the stem and transom. Use this as a guide to the amount of bevel to allow in each frame notch. Mark the bevels and remove the gunwale while the bevels are cut for both gunwales. Mark and cut the gunwale parallel with the side of the stem (fig. 23, 2). Fix the gunwales to the stem and the frames, then cut to length and fit into the notches on the transom. Fix the chines (B) in the same way (Photo 13). Fix the risers (F) from frame 1 to the transom.

At this stage it is advisable to test the stiffness of various parts. Although there will be adequate strength when all of the parts are finally fixed together, it is possible during the fixing of the skin to exert considerable pressure on parts of the framework so that they are damaged or broken. One or two temporary struts under the hog will prevent distortion when pressing down on it. With some woods there may be a tendency for the gunwale to spring inwards under the pressure of fitting the skin between frame 1 and the stem. This can be prevented by nailing a temporary strut across the gunwales midway between the frame and the stem. Leave this strut in place until after the boat is turned over.

Fair off all surfaces on which the plywood skin will

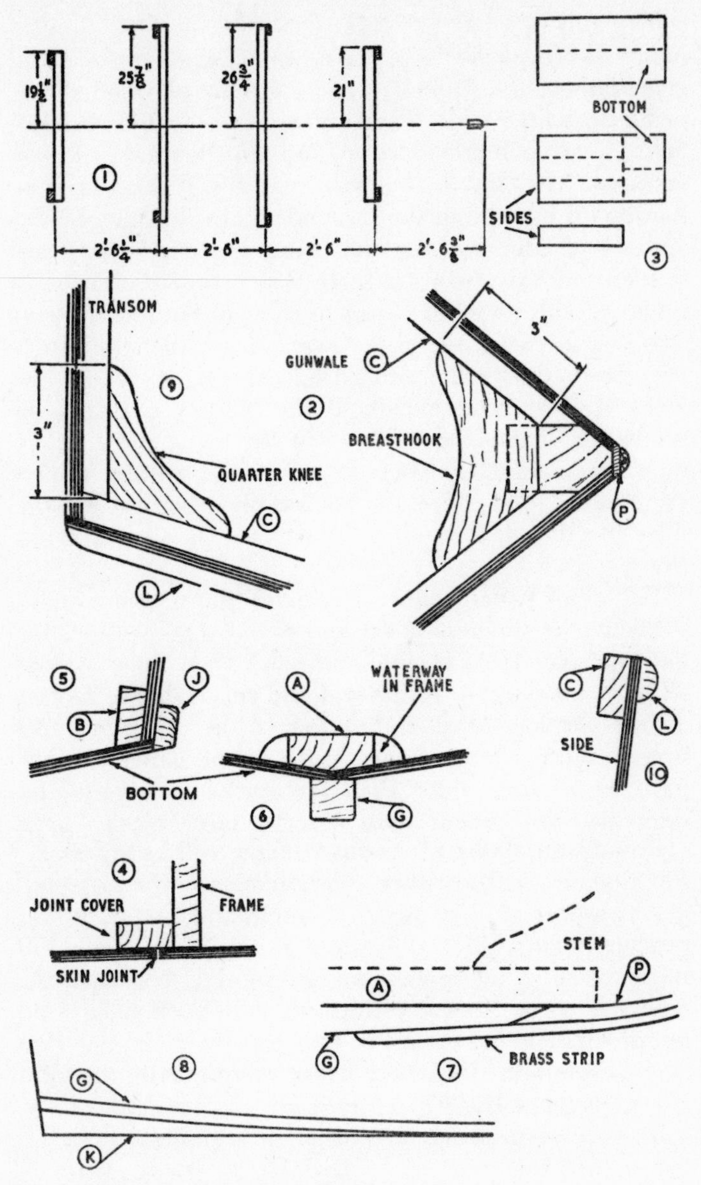

19½"
25⅞"
26¾"
21"
1
2'-6¼"
2'-6"
2'-6"
2'-6⅜"
BOTTOM
SIDES
3
TRANSOM
3"
9
QUARTER KNEE
C
L
GUNWALE
C
2
BREASTHOOK
3"
P
5
J
B
BOTTOM
A
WATERWAY IN FRAME
6
G
C
L
SIDE
10
4
JOINT COVER
FRAME
SKIN JOINT
STEM
A
P
G
BRASS STRIP
7
G
8
K

Fig. 23

rest (photo 14). Pay particular attention to those coming under the edges of sheets. Carry any fairing off down the extensions of the frames to allow for the plywood sheets being cut a little wide. Towards the stem the plywood will follow a curve in cross-section, and this should be allowed for when bevelling in that area. A piece of cardboard or hardboard may be sprung around to give an idea of the amount of curve. Along the chine, the bevel matching frame 1 will have to be gradually widened until eventually it allows both plywood panels to come in line at the stem.

If long plywood sheets are available, full-length panels may be used, but if standard 8 ft. sheets are used, they will cut most economically if the bottom is joined on frame 3 and the sides on frame 2 (fig. 23, 3 and 4). The sides are completely covered before the bottom panels are fitted. At the chines the bottom plywood overlaps the sides and the exposed edges are covered by rubbing strips (fig. 23, 5).

Put an aft panel against the side so that it comes about halfway over the joint cover and overlaps gunwale, chine and transom. Hold it close and mark on it the shapes of all parts touching it. Remove it and cut to shape, leaving a little surplus. Mark the outline of the opposite panel from it, but mark the shapes on the second panel from the parts of its own side. Drill for screws at about 3 in. intervals. Experiment with a scrap piece of the same plywood to test whether countersinking will be necessary. Put glue on the framework and hardener on the plywood, if a two-part glue is used. Assemble and put screws at random points quickly. Cramps may also be used. Fill the gaps until all screws are driven. For economy the screws may be at wider intervals and brass nails used intermediately. Make and fit the opposite panel. See that corners are tight. Use extra screws there and on the joint cover, as necessary.

The forward panels are fitted in a similar way, but because of the twist it is advisable to leave plenty of surplus at the first cutting and to experiment before final cutting. There should be a tight butt joint over frame 2. About 18 in. from the stem along the chine the joint between bottom and side panels will change from a lap to a mitre. (fig. 14 E and F). At this stage allow for this by leaving at least $\frac{1}{4}$ in. of the side panel projecting above the centre line of the chine.

After the sides have been completely covered, let the glue set, then level off the plywood with the chine, ready to take the bottom panels, except for the forward mitred joint. The angle of this joint will change as it bisects the the angle between the panels until the edge becomes a right-angle at the stem. Trim this angle with a rebate plane or a chisel.

Make and fit the aft bottom panels, letting them come halfway over the joint cover on frame 3. They should meet on the centre-line of the hog and overlap the chines and the transom. When marking the forward panels it may be advisable to use a cardboard template for the twisted part from just aft of frame 1 to the stem. Allow for the mitre, with a notch so that the part aft of it may overlap sufficiently (fig. 14 E). Make a trial fitting of the plywood panel. If it is stubborn, bend it part way and leave it cramped down, then try bending it further. If necessary, use a cloth soaked in hot water on the outside. Glue and screw in place, using screws spaced fairly close together at the parts of greatest curvature (photo 15).

Level off the plywood along the chines. Glue and screw on the chine rubbers (J) (fig. 23, 5). They may be carried right up to the stem, or cut off just forward of where the joint changes from a lap to a mitre. Much depends on the workmanship of the mitre. If this is a good fit it may be exposed, but if this tricky job has not finished very successfully, the rubber will make good the joint and protect it.

Level the plywood at the centre to take the keel (G) (fig. 23, 6). Plane off to give a width sufficient for the keel to bed down evenly. Taper the keel forward, both in width and thickness to about $\frac{1}{2}$ in. square. Fix it with glue and counterbored screws driven from outside. Fit the stem band (P), allowing it to overlap the bevelled end of the keel (fig. 23, 7). Fix it with nails driven centrally. When the glue has set, level the sides of the stem band flush with the plywood. It is an aid in keeping the boat on its course and some protection when dragging the boat by the stem, to have a skeg (K) aft. This is a tapered piece, glued and screwed on the keel (fig. 23, 8).

The bottom rubbers (H and I) are a few inches shorter than the bottom stiffeners (D and E). They extend from the transom forward and their forward ends should be tapered in the same way as the keel. Fix them with glue and screws centrally over the stiffeners.

To reduce or prevent dirt absorption by the hull when it is turned over, all of the outside may be given one coat of varnish or priming paint at this stage. If this is to be done, screw heads should be covered with stopping, if desired, and the whole surface given a good sanding first.

Unfasten the boat from the floor and turn it over (photo 16). Support it evenly with chocks or wedges. Cramp a temporary strip across the gunwales or the top of frame 2, then cut the extensions off all the frames, the transom and the stem. The strut should be left in place, to prevent the hull distorting, until after the central thwart has been fixed. Level the side plywood with the gunwales. Remove any surplus glue from the inside.

Knees have to be made and fixed in the corners of the transom (fig. 23, 9) and there should be another (called a "breast-hook") at the stem (fig. 23, 2). The top of the stem must be notched to clear it. Fix the knees with glue and screws driven from outside.

Make the thwarts (M and O). Notch them around the frames. Fit them, and the sternsheets (N) close to the skin and screw them to the risers (F). As there is a tendency to lift boats by the thwarts, strips may be glued and

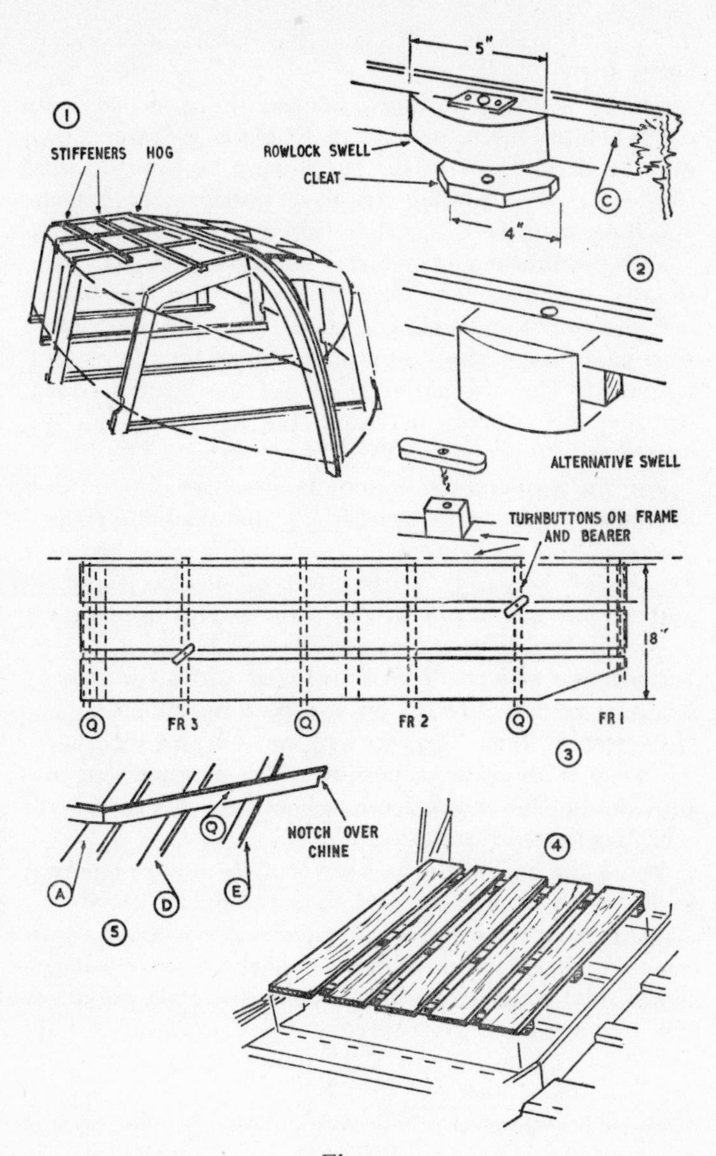
1
STIFFENERS
HOG
ROWLOCK SWELL
CLEAT
5"
4"
C
2
ALTERNATIVE SWELL
TURNBUTTONS ON FRAME AND BEARER
18"
Q
FR 3
Q
FR 2
Q
FR 1
3
NOTCH OVER CHINE
Q
A
D
E
5
4

Fig. 24

screwed through the skin above the thwarts if desired or knees fitted.

At the rowlock positions thicken the gunwales with swells before drilling and fitting the plates. Separate cleats may be fixed below or the swells may be built up solid (fig. 24, 2). Fix rubbing strips (L) outside the gunwales and flush with their top edges (fig. 23, 10).

Two possible arrangements of bottom boards are shown (fig. 24, 3 and 4). The simplest arrangement has boards laid fore and aft in two long sections, resting on the frames. This keeps them above any bilge water, but leg room is restricted. The alternative is to put the bottom boards between the frames, increasing the leg room, but not offering much protection from bilge water.

For the two-section bottom boards (fig. 24, 3) it is advisable to put extra bearers (Q) between the frames. These rest on the bottom stiffeners and are notched over the chines (fig. 24, 5). Turnbuttons on blocks on frame 3 and the forward bearer will hold the boards in place.

Bottom boards to fit between the frames (fig. 24, 4) are better made with the boards arranged athwartships in six sections, resting directly on the bottom stiffeners. The strips joining them then go fore and aft and the boards are as near the skin as possible. This arrangement also provides notches which serve as heel rests. Fix the boards with blocks and turnbuttons.

Finish the boat with three coats of varnish, or one coat each primer, undercoat and top coat paint (photo 17). A painted exterior and a varnished interior looks smart. Another alternative is to have a dark colour outside, a lighter matching one inside, but the thwarts and bottom boards varnished. At the stem carry a piece of half-round brass from the top of the stem post to aft of where the stem band joins the keel (fig. 23, 7). If the boat is likely to be dragged much over pebbles or concrete the brass strip may be taken the whole length of the keel.

Fit lanyards to the rowlocks and attach a rope painter

to the hole in the stem. If the boat is to be towed, fix a ringbolt through the stem just below the chine position.

Oars may be about 6 ft. 6 in., and made as described in Chapter 11. If rowed by one pair of oars, they should be used in the aft position when single-handed. With one or two passengers it may be better to row from the forward position, depending on the relative weights of the oarsman and the others. In this case the oars should be about 6 ft. 6 in. long. If two pairs of oars are to be used, those for the forward position could be shortened to 6 ft. or 5 ft. 6 in. If the boat is likely to be used regularly by two oarsmen, it may be worthwhile having a rudder so that a passenger may steer. The rudder described for "Pete" would do, but it might be easier to handle if a yoke was fitted instead of the tiller (fig. 22). The helmsman could then sit centrally and face forward.

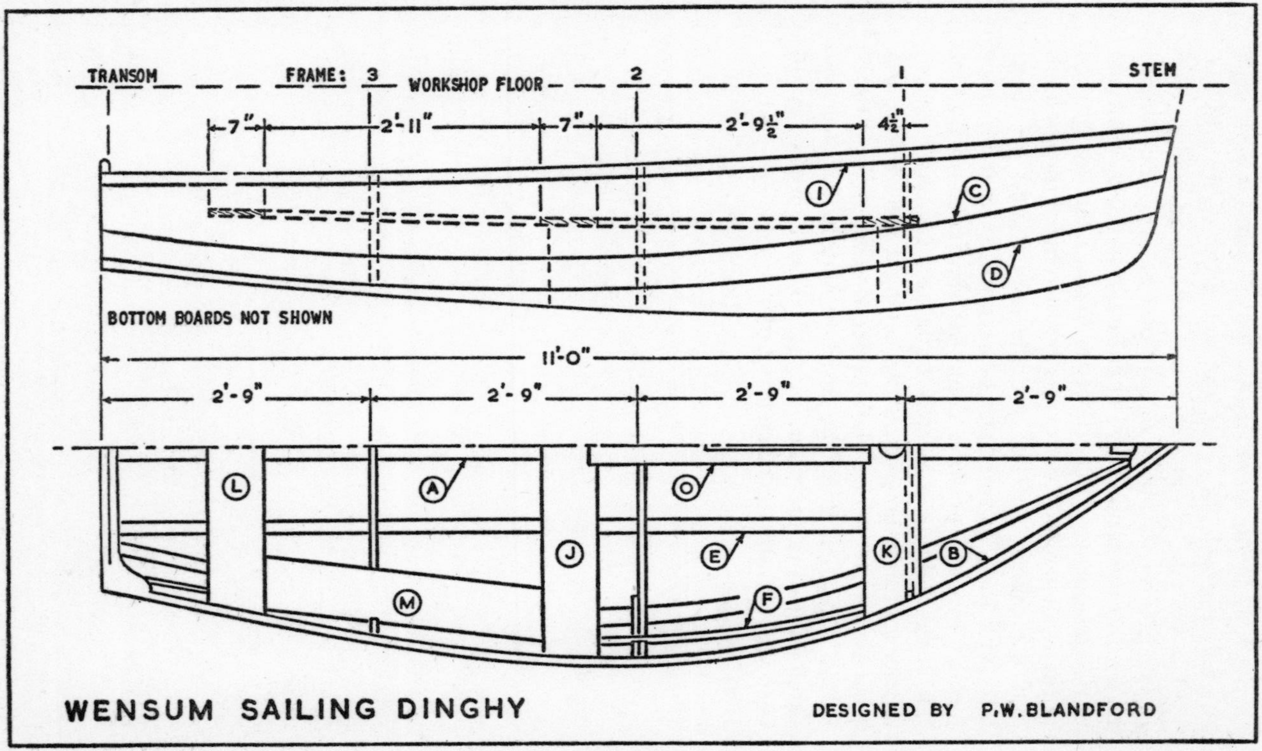

TRANSOM

FRAME: 3 WORKSHOP FLOOR 2 1

STEM

7" 2'-11" 7" 2'-9½" 4½"

BOTTOM BOARDS NOT SHOWN

11'-0"

2'-9" 2'-9" 2'-9" 2'-9"

I C D L A O J E K B M F

WENSUM SAILING DINGHY

DESIGNED BY P.W. BLANDFORD

Fig. 25

Chapter 8

WENSUM—
11 FT. DOUBLE-CHINE SAILING DINGHY
Building the boat

A DOUBLE-CHINE hull gives a better performance in broken water than a single-chine boat, as the form is nearer to the rounded sections which cannot be obtained in ordinary plywood boat building. Construction may take a little longer than a single-chine boat of the same size, but in many ways it is easier to make a good job.

Wensum is a general-purpose sailing dinghy (fig. 25). With its gunter rig it is a good family boat with ample stability, and a good turn of speed. If it is given a Bermudan rig it has a good turn of speed and is a very sporty craft. Decking is advised for racing, but apart from that the boat is the same for either rig. Without decking, Wensum may be used as a yacht's dinghy, a camping boat or a family knock-about craft on inland or coastal waters. It may be built as a rowing boat (photo 19) and the sailing gear added afterwards, but it is simpler to include the centreboard case during construction, even if the addition of sailing gear is not intended immediately. The boat is easy to row by one or two oarsmen, or it may be propelled by a small outboard motor of up to 3 h.p. The boat is not suitable for a large motor. Although Wensum may be carried on a car roof rack, most builders find it more convenient on a trailer which can also be used for launching.

The boat is built upside-down on frames which are attached to the floor in the same way as described for Corrib. A floor space at least 12 ft. by 6 ft. is needed to allow room for fixing the boat down and working on it.

As with the other boats, all joints are made with screws or nails and synthetic resin glue.

Make the frames, transom and stem (fig. 26). Notice that although most sections are flat, the skin blends into a curve at the transom and the shaping of the bottom panel over frame 1 gives a slight curve. A full-size drawing of frames, transom and stem is available (see Preface). All of the temporary crossbars and the joint covers at hog and chines are on the aft sides. If a centreboard case is to be fitted, the hog joint cover on frame 2 is only a temporary one and it should not be glued. Cut all recesses square at this stage. Edges may all be cut square and faired off later, except that the sides and chine parts of frame 1 may be given a preliminary bevel. The transom is solid wood or plywood with framing attached to it. The recesses are cut in the framing only. In this boat the transom is vertical and the temporary strut on the floor has its edge square. The stem may be cut from a solid piece or built up from several pieces fixed together. Plane the forward edge to the approximate bevels.

Mark out the workshop floor (fig. 27, 1) and assemble the frames and other parts on it. Sight along to check that the stem is upright and the frames line up correctly. If necessary, put a stiff plank over the struts and alongside the stem. Check that the frames are at right-angles to the centre-line and are standing upright.

Make and fit the hog (A) (fig. 27, 2). Taper it slightly in width for about 2 ft. to the width of the stem. Use the frames as a guide to the angle to plane on the underside of the hog. Fasten the hog to the stem with glue and screws, then bend it into place and fix it to the frames before cutting to length and fitting to the transom. At frames 2 and 3 the recess is widened to make waterways alongside the hog, to allow bilge water to run to the lowest point. At frame 1 this effect is obtained by putting the frame on top of the hog. At the transom the hog fits close in its recess.

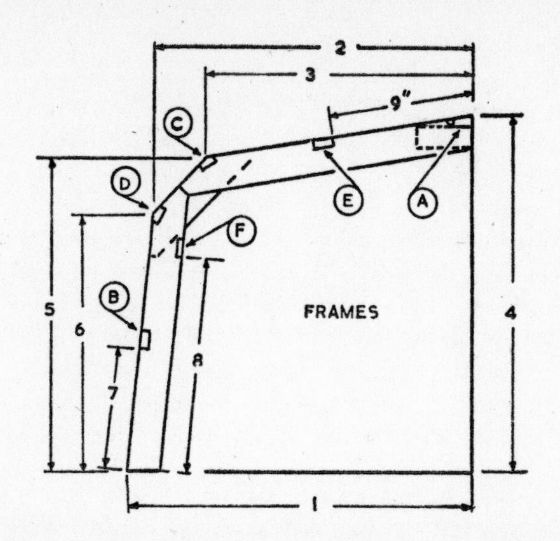

INCHES	1	2	3	4	5	6	7	8
FRAME 1	$22\frac{3}{4}$	$18\frac{5}{8}$	$15\frac{1}{4}$	29	$22\frac{3}{4}$	$18\frac{1}{8}$	8	$16\frac{7}{8}$
FRAME 2	$28\frac{3}{4}$	$26\frac{1}{2}$	$22\frac{3}{4}$	$29\frac{1}{8}$	$25\frac{5}{8}$	$21\frac{1}{8}$	$9\frac{3}{4}$	$17\frac{5}{8}$
FRAME 3	26	$23\frac{3}{8}$	$19\frac{1}{2}$	$25\frac{7}{8}$	$24\frac{1}{8}$	$20\frac{5}{8}$	$10\frac{3}{4}$	$16\frac{7}{8}$
TRANSOM	$20\frac{1}{4}$	$16\frac{7}{8}$	$12\frac{7}{8}$	$22\frac{3}{4}$	$21\frac{3}{8}$	$18\frac{1}{8}$	$11\frac{1}{4}$	$15\frac{7}{8}$

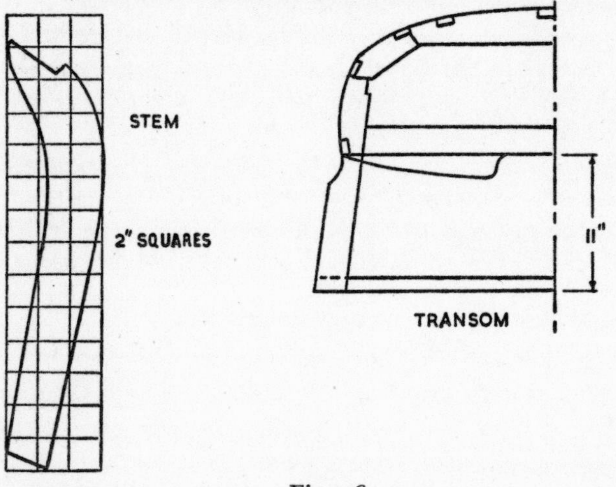

Fig. 26

If the bottom stiffeners (E) are fixed next they will hold the frames in position. They should extend through frame 1 about 2 in. Check that the frames are true and square at this stage. There should be little fear of them moving afterwards. The stiffeners and all other parts fit into slots and are glued and screwed there. Fairing off is simplified if the lengthwise parts are let in deep enough to either come flush or to leave a little to be faired off the frames.

When fitting the gunwales and chines it is advisable to start at the stem and make the tightest bend first. Bend a gunwale (B) approximately to shape. Cut it to fit against the stem, then glue and screw it there (fig. 28, 1). Cut the other gunwale to the same angle and fit that. Bend them to fit into the slots in the frames. Bevel the slots to take the parts. If a gunwale is stubborn, pull it part way and tie it. If necessary wrap a cloth soaked in hot water around the part which has to take a greater bend, or use one of the techniques described in Chapter 5. If necessary use cramps at the stem and frame joints before finally fixing. Cut to length and fit into the transom slots after bending through the frame slots. Fit the two risers (F) from frame 1 (far enough forward to take the thwart) to the transom.

Fix the two pairs of chines (C and D) in a similar way to the gunwales. They may be given a preliminary bevel, using the frame angles as a guide. Mark a centre line on each to ensure the bevels being even (fig. 28, 2). Temporary bending with cramps will show what bevelling is needed in the frame slots.

Fair off the framework to take the plywood skin (photos 18, 20). Check in all directions with a straight-edge or long strip of wood. Towards the ends let this follow the curve the plywood will take. Make sure the bevels on the chines meet. There should be no flat left between the two bevels. Make sure there are no high spots, particularly over the end grain of chine joint covers and that the plywood will bed down closely over the transom and other exposed edges.

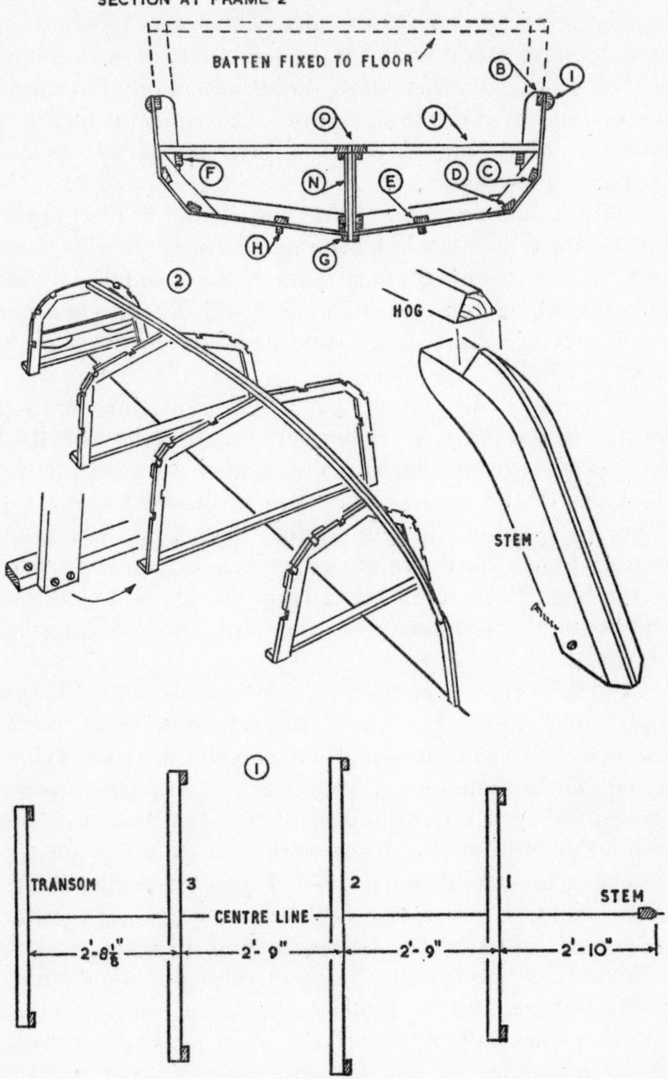
SECTION AT FRAME 2
BATTEN FIXED TO FLOOR
B
I
O
J
F
N
E
D
C
H
G
2
HOG
STEM
1
TRANSOM
3
2
1
STEM
CENTRE LINE
2'-8$\frac{1}{8}$"
2'-9"
2'-9"
2'-10"

Fig. 27

The skin is made up from standard 8 ft. sheets. The bottom is joined along the centre of the hog. The bottom and sides are made with 8 ft. panels taken as far forward as they will come, then short pieces joined on. The chine pieces join on the middle frame. The order of fitting is bottom, chine, side; with each fitted completely before moving on to the next.

The two large bottom panels may be cut from opposite sides of the same sheet. The triangle between their forward ends will make one forward part of the bottom. The aft side panels and two parts of a chine will cut from another sheet, leaving sufficient for rudder sides. The other parts will cut from a third sheet.

For economy in cutting, paper templates may be used for the shaped parts. Mark out panels in the way described for Corrib, except that the sheets have to meet on the thickness of the chines. They can be marked along the edge of the chine and $\frac{3}{4}$ in. added (fig. 28, 3). The large bottom panels have straight edges meeting on the centre of the hog. Their outer edges come to the centres of the chines and the positions of all other parts should be marked on them.

Drill for screws at about 4 in. intervals around the edges and about 7 in. pitch over stiffeners and other parts. Reduce the spacing to about 2 in. on the transom. When fixing the bottom panels keep screws away from where the centreboard slot will come, if a sailing boat is being built. Put glue on the framework and hardener on the plywood, then fix down the panel quickly, using cramps and weights if necessary to hold it temporarily while screws are driven at key points, then at all holes.

Where the joints come in the panels put joint covers inside between the lengthwise parts (fig. 28, 4). These may be pieces of chine material or wider pieces of plywood. Make templates for the forward triangles and cut the wood with a little to spare. Start by fixing to the joint covers. Progress forward from there, screwing to the

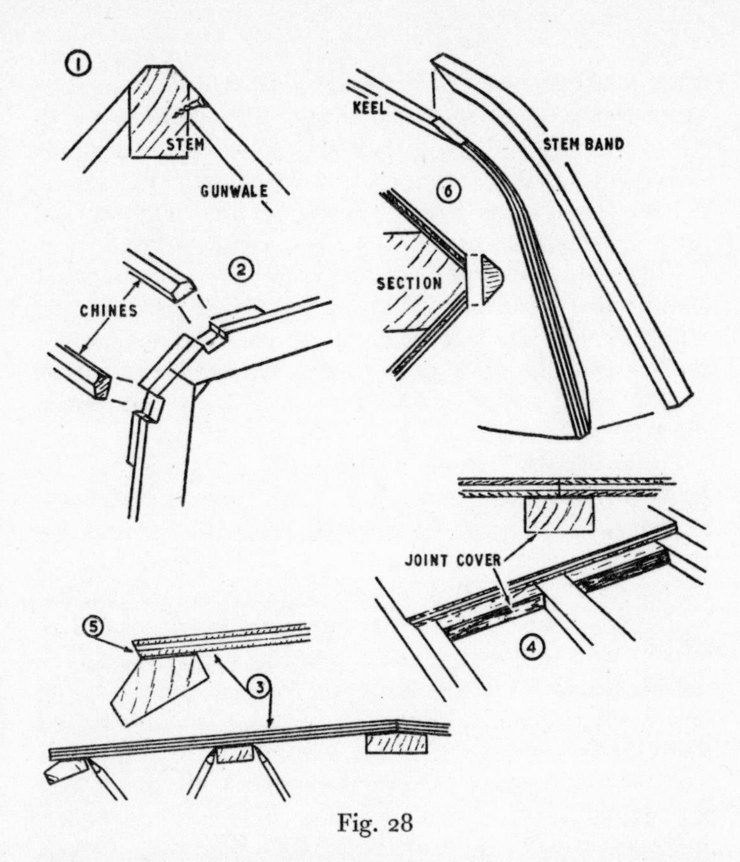

Fig. 28

frame, chine and hog. Pull the plywood to the framework and hold it with cramps as you screw. Screws will have to be closer than elsewhere. If the plywood is stubborn, use a cloth soaked in hot water.

After fixing the full length of both sides of the bottom and allowing the glue to set, prepare the edges of the plywood to take the chine panels. Use a rebate plane, or any other plane with its blade the full width of the sole, to plane the plywood edges back to the centreline of the chine piece at an angle that will mitre with the next panel (fig. 28, 5).

Mark a chine panel, arranging the joint to come on frame 2. At first cut the piece too wide and plane its edge to make a good fit against the edge of the bottom panel. When a satisfactory joint is obtained, mark the final shape of the part, then cut and fit it. Make the other chine panels. There is not much twist at the stem and no difficulty should be experienced. Prepare the mitred edges.

Make the side panels in the same way. Fit the joint against the chine panel before finally cutting to shape, although with the sides it does not matter about cutting exactly to the gunwale as this can be trimmed later. Make an 8 ft. side panel from the transom forward and join in short pieces in the same way as the bottom.

Plane off the surplus plywood at the stem and the transom. Along the centre line plane down the plywood to form a surface for the keel (G). This is 2 in. wide for the greater part of its length, but it is tapered forward (photo 21). Fix it with glue and counterbored screws, but keep screws away from where the centre board slot will be cut. There is sufficient width of wood for them to be driven outside the width of the slot. Right forward the end of the keel is bevelled and a stem band bent to shape and nailed and glued on (fig. 28, 6). This is best made of ash, which may bend in one piece, or it can be built up of two laminations.

Disconnect the boat from the floor and turn it over. Support it evenly. Before cutting off the frame extensions, cramp or nail a temporary piece across frame 2 or the gunwales amidships. This is to prevent distortion and should remain in place until after the centre thwart has been fitted.

After cutting off the extensions, plane down the plywood level with the gunwales. Make and fit the knees at the corners of the transom and the breasthook (fig. 23, 2 and 9). If decking is to be fitted, leave the tops of the frames square, but if the boat is to remain open, they should be rounded.

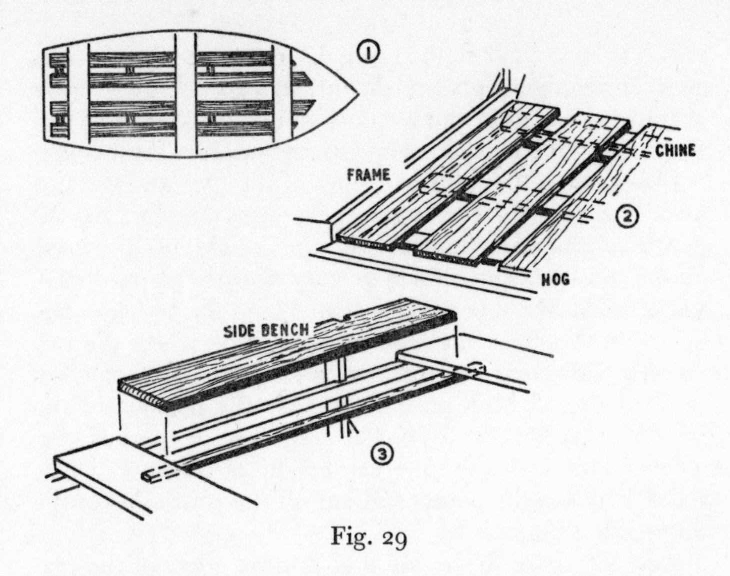

Fig. 29

If the boat is not to be equipped for sailing, the three thwarts may be fitted now (J, K, L). Screw them to the risers. Thicken the gunwales with rowlock swells 12 in. aft of the edges of the thwarts. Drill and fix the rowlock plates (fig. 24, 2). Protect the outside of the gunwale with a rubbing strip (I) screwed on. Alternatively, use rubber moulding.

In racing boats bottom boards are sometimes omitted, but for general purposes it is wiser to fit them, to spread the load of the crew and to prevent local strain. The simplest bottom boards consist of strips laid lengthwise over the frames (fig. 29, 1), but it is neater and there is more leg room if the bottom boards are made up to fit between the frames (fig. 29, 2). Use blocks and turn-buttons to locate and secure the bottom boards.

If the boat is likely to be dragged over pebbles, rubbing strips (H) should be screwed over the bottom stiffeners.

If the boat is to be equipped for sailing, either immediately or later, it is simplest to fit the centre-board case before fitting the thwarts, although it is not impossible to add one to a boat built originally only for rowing. The general arrangements are shown (fig. 30, 1). The centre of frame 2 has to be cut away to admit the case, and this should be done after removing the temporary joint cover.

Make one of the plywood sides of the case and use this as a template for the other parts and the slot. As the depth of the case depends on the height of the risers above the hog, and this may vary slightly in particular boats, make the side wide at first. Plane the bottom edge to match the slight curve of the hog. Mark where the two thwarts will come on the two risers and lay a piece of wood across in each position so that the position of the thwarts over the centre-board case may be marked (fig. 30, 2). This will also give the height of the case. Draw a line between the points and cut off the waste. Make the other side to match.

Add the strips to the top and bottom edges of the plywood, then join the parts with the spacing pieces between. Mark the position of the slot in the hog. Drill $\frac{5}{8}$ in. holes at each end of the slot and a few more near one end so that a space may be made to admit a saw (fig. 30, 3). Turn the boat over and mark the width of the slot on the keel, then saw away the waste, keeping on the inside of the lines. Do not finish the slot completely to width at this stage.

With the boat the right way up, fix the centre-board case in position temporarily with a few screws. Make the two thwarts. The mast thwart has a hole cut to take the mast. Both are notched to take the gangboard which comes over the centre-board case. When the assembly is satisfactory dismantle it. Coat the underside of the case and the hog with a jointing compound and screw down on to this a little at a time so that the compound is compressed evenly. Fix the thwarts with glue and screws. Trim the slot in the keel and hog to match the inside of the case.

The mast step is a block the same height as the joint

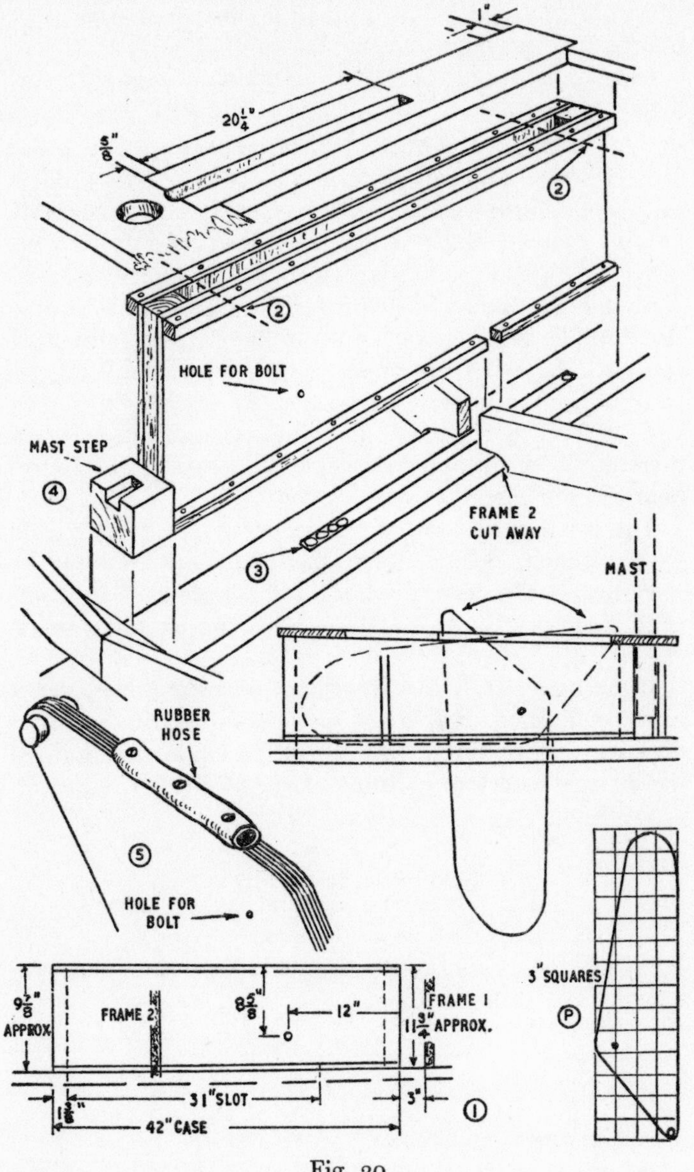
1"
20¼"
⅝"
2
2
HOLE FOR BOLT
MAST STEP
4
FRAME 2
CUT AWAY
3
MAST
RUBBER
HOSE
5
HOLE FOR
BOLT
9⅞"
APPROX.
FRAME 2
8⅝"
12"
FRAME 1
11¾" APPROX.
1⅜"
31" SLOT
3"
42" CASE
1
3" SQUARES
P

Fig. 30

cover on frame 1, fixed between the frame and the case, with a mortise in its top (fig. 30, 4).

The centre-board pivots on a bolt through the case. It is kept in place by friction and operated by moving its top. Make the centre-board (P). Bevel the parts which will project below the boat and round their edges. Glue blocks each side to form handles at the top. Make a trial assembly and see that the board swings fully down and up into the case. Varnish or paint the board before final assembly. A piece of cloth on a batten may be used to varnish inside the case. To hold the board in position a piece of rubber or plastic hose is screwed on to provide friction. Adjustment of friction is made by turning the screws (fig. 30, 5). Use large washers under the bolt head and nut, and bed them down in jointing compound when fixing the centre-board in the case.

The usual position of the helmsman when sailing is on a side bench (M) between the main thwart and the sternsheets. The bench rests on the riser and its front edge is supported by a strip screwed under the thwarts (fig. 29, 3).

If the boat is to be used without decking (photo 22) it may be finished with paint or varnish to choice, but if decking is to be fitted, this should be made as described in Chapter 10 before painting or varnishing is completed.

Chapter 9

WENSUM—
11 FT. DOUBLE-CHINE SAILING DINGHY
Sailing gear—Gunter rig

THE rudder of a sailing boat needs to be deep to be effective. In anything but the smallest sizes this means that it is liable to hit the bottom earlier than may be expected. Of course, this may damage the rudder or even cause a capsize. If the rudder has to be removed in shallow water, control is lost. To reduce these troubles the blade of the rudder may be made to swing up between the cheeks of the stock. A metal rudder blade will stay down under its own weight, but a wooden blade needs some sort of springing to keep it down. This can be provided by a stout piece of rubber. In either case, the blade is free to swing up if it hits anything and it will drop back again as the water deepens. If a light line is taken from a hole in the aft edge of the blade, the blade may be fixed up when required. The raised blade provides limited control.

Make the blade from $\frac{3}{8}$ in. or $\frac{1}{2}$ in. plywood and thoroughly round all the edges which come below the stock (fig. 31, 1). The stock is built up from three pieces. The cheeks may be $\frac{1}{4}$ in. or $\frac{3}{8}$ in. plywood. The filler piece should be the same thickness as the blade, or slightly thicker. If it is the same thickness a piece of stout paper glued in each joint will make up the thickness sufficiently to allow the blade to swing easily. Notice that there is a screw in the stock to act as a stop for the notched part of the blade (fig. 31, 2). The rubber passes through a hole in the blade and the loop is secured by a tight whipping of stout thread. The other end goes over a hook at the top

WENSUM

11 FT. DOUBLE-CHINE SAILING DINGHY

Material Schedule

Frames are numbered. Main structural parts are lettered. All plywood should be of marine quality—in Great Britain marked BSS 1088. Many woods may be used for building this boat. Mahogany looks smart and is the best choice for most parts if the boat is to be varnished, but cheaper woods may be used as indicated if preferred. Spruce bends more easily than mahogany. Bottom boards may be any cheap soft wood. Suggested woods are:

S	Sitka spruce or yellow cedar
D	Red deal
M	Mahogany
P	Parana pine
O	Oak or aframosia
A	Ash or rock elm

Part	*Name*	*Number required*	*Length ft.*	*in.*	*Width in.*	*Thickness in.*	*Wood*
	Stem	1	2	3	6	$1\frac{1}{2}$	P
	Frame 1	2	1	10	$2\frac{3}{8}$	$\frac{3}{4}$	P
		2	1	8	$2\frac{3}{8}$	$\frac{3}{4}$	P
		2	1	0	$2\frac{3}{8}$	$\frac{3}{4}$	P
		1	1	5	$2\frac{3}{8}$	$\frac{3}{4}$	P
	Frame 2	2	2	1	$2\frac{3}{8}$	$\frac{3}{4}$	P
		2	2	2	$2\frac{3}{8}$	$\frac{3}{4}$	P
		3	1	0	$2\frac{3}{8}$	$\frac{3}{4}$	P
	Frame 3	2	2	0	$2\frac{3}{8}$	$\frac{3}{4}$	P
		2	1	11	$2\frac{3}{8}$	$\frac{3}{4}$	P
		3	1	0	$2\frac{3}{8}$	$\frac{3}{4}$	P
	Transom	2	1	7	$2\frac{3}{8}$	$\frac{3}{4}$	P
		1	2	2	$2\frac{3}{8}$	$\frac{3}{4}$	P
		1	2	9	$2\frac{3}{8}$	$\frac{3}{4}$	P

		2		8	$2\frac{3}{8}$	$\frac{3}{4}$	P
		1	3	0	14	$\frac{7}{8}$	M
	Floor battens	4	5	0	$1\frac{7}{8}$	$\frac{7}{8}$	D
A	Hog	1	11	0	$2\frac{7}{8}$	$\frac{7}{8}$	M or S
B	Gunwales	2	12	0	$1\frac{3}{8}$	$\frac{5}{8}$	S
C	Chines, upper	2	12	0	$1\frac{3}{8}$	$\frac{3}{4}$	S
D	Chines, lower	2	12	0	$1\frac{3}{8}$	$\frac{3}{4}$	S
E	Bottom stiffeners	2	9	0	$1\frac{3}{8}$	$\frac{5}{8}$	S or D
F	Risers	2	9	0	$1\frac{3}{8}$	$\frac{5}{8}$	S or M
G	Keel	1	11	0	2	$\frac{3}{4}$	O or P
H	Bottom rubbers	2	7	0	$\frac{3}{4}$	$\frac{3}{4}$	O or P
I	Gunwale rubbers	2	12	0	$\frac{7}{8}$	half-round	M
J	Main thwart	1	4	6	$6\frac{7}{8}$	$\frac{7}{8}$	M or D
K	Mast thwart	1	3	6	$6\frac{7}{8}$	$\frac{7}{8}$	M or D
L	Stern sheets	1	3	6	$6\frac{7}{8}$	$\frac{7}{8}$	M or D
M	Side benches	2	3	0	$6\frac{7}{8}$	$\frac{7}{8}$	M or D
	Side benches	2	3	6	$1\frac{3}{8}$	$\frac{5}{8}$	M or D
N	Centre-board case	2	3	7	12	$\frac{3}{8}$	plywood
		2	1	0	$1\frac{3}{8}$	$\frac{3}{4}$	M or D
		4	3	7	$\frac{5}{8}$	$\frac{5}{8}$	M or D
O	Gangboard	1	3	6	4	$\frac{7}{8}$	M or D
P	Centre-board	1	3	6	12	$\frac{5}{8}$	plywood
	Stem band	1	2	3	$1\frac{1}{8}$	$\frac{1}{2}$	A
	Bottom boards cut from	15	3	6	$4\frac{7}{8}$	$\frac{1}{2}$	D
	Bottom boards cut from	6	4	9	$1\frac{3}{8}$	$\frac{1}{2}$	D
	Rudder	1	2	0	12	$\frac{3}{8}$	plywood
		2	1	3	6	$\frac{1}{4}$	plywood
		1		9	5	$\frac{3}{8}$	plywood
	Tiller	1	3	6	$1\frac{1}{4}$	$\frac{7}{8}$	A
	Skin	3	8	0	48	$\frac{1}{4}$	plywood
	Mast	1	10	6	$2\frac{1}{2}$	$2\frac{1}{2}$	S
	Boom	1	8	6	$1\frac{3}{4}$	$1\frac{3}{4}$	S
	Gaff	1	10	6	$1\frac{3}{4}$	$1\frac{1}{2}$	S

WENSUM

11 FT. DOUBLE-CHINE SAILING DINGHY

continued

Small parts cut from waste

Mast step	1	2⅜	2⅜	2⅜	M or D
Rowlock swells	4	5	2⅜	⅝	M
Rowlock swells	4	5	1	⅝	M
Knees	3	7	4	¾	O or P
Gaff jaws	2	10	6	⅜	plywood
Mast chocks	2	2½	⅝	½	O
Skin joint covers	6	9	1⅜	⅝	S

Other materials

Rubber or plastic hose	1	5	⅝	outside diameter
Brass bolt, washer and nut	1	2	⅜	diameter
Brass bolt, washer and nut	1	1½	¼	diameter
Brass sheet	1	6	4	20 gauge
Brass cotter pins	2	1¼	⅛	diameter
Rubber	1	12	¼	

Sundries

1 gross 1¼ in. × 6 gauge countersunk brass screws (frames, etc.).

3 gross ⅝ in. × 4 gauge countersunk brass screws (skin).

2 dozen 1½ in. × 6 gauge countersunk brass screws (hog, chines).

2 dozen 2 in. × 8 gauge countersunk brass screws (thwarts).

6 dozen ¾ in. × 6 gauge countersunk brass screws (fittings, skin).

(or annular ring nails, see page 50)

$\frac{1}{2}$ lb. 1$\frac{1}{4}$ in. copper boat nails (bottom boards).
$\frac{1}{4}$ lb. $\frac{3}{4}$ in. brass shoe nails (skin, centre-board case).
1 tube Seelastik.
Approximately 2 lb. synthetic resin glue.
$\frac{1}{4}$ lb. plastic wood or waterproof stopping.
3 pints marine varnish.
1 pint priming paint, 1 pint undercoat, 1 pint top coat.

Fittings and rigging

2 pairs 2 in. rowlocks and plates.
(7 ft. oars are suitable).
1 set gudgeons and pintles to suit a $\frac{7}{8}$ in. rudder.
2 cleats 3 in.
1 sheave 1$\frac{1}{2}$ in.
1 light gooseneck fitting.
3 single-sheave, single-becket blocks to suit 1$\frac{1}{4}$ in. rope.
4 eye plates.
2 shackles $\frac{3}{16}$ in.
3 thimbles for $\frac{1}{8}$ in. diameter wire rope.
3 thimbles for 1$\frac{1}{4}$ in. circumference rope.
30 ft. flexible wire rope, $\frac{3}{32}$ in. or $\frac{1}{8}$ in. diameter.
24 ft. manila rope, 1$\frac{1}{4}$ in. circumference.
50 ft. cotton rope, 1$\frac{1}{4}$ in. circumference.
1 hank light lashing line.
Sails as drawing.

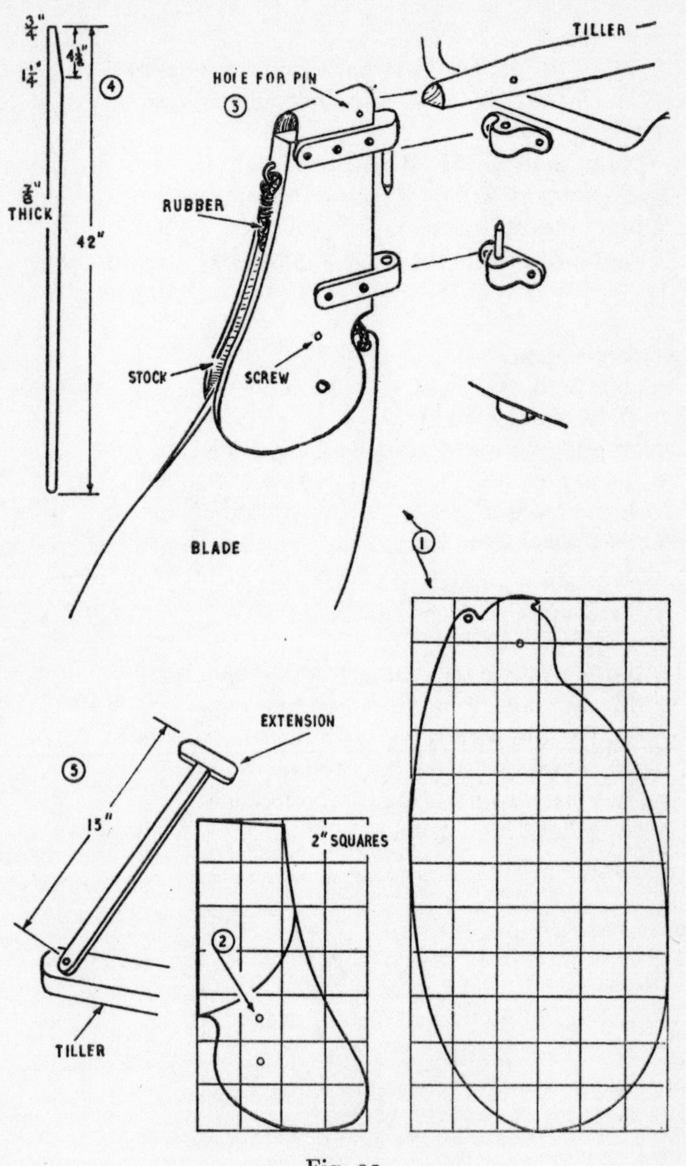

TILLER
HOLE FOR PIN
3
4
RUBBER
THICK
42"
STOCK
SCREW
BLADE
1
EXTENSION
5
15"
2" SQUARES
2
TILLER

Fig. 31

of the stock. To lengthen the life of the rubber, leave it off the hook when the rudder is out of use.

The tiller rests on top of the stock and is held by a brass band (fig. 31, 3). Projections at the top should be avoided, as the main sheet tends to catch on them. Use ash or oak for the tiller (fig. 31, 4). Shape one end to fit in the brass band, and taper the other part to round. Drill a hole through the brass and the tiller to take a brass cotter pin, which can have a retaining line fixed to a small screw eye in the stock. For sailing with the first rig described a plain tiller will do, but for the more ambitious Bermudan rig an extension allows sitting out (fig. 31, 5).

The rudder has to be hinged on the transom and several types of hangings are available. Those shown are known as gudgeons (the parts with holes) and pintles (the parts with pins). Both parts on the rudder may have pins, or there may be one hole and one pin. It may be necessary to groove the rudder stock to take the nearest standard size fittings available. The top fittings can also locate and fix the brass band over the tiller. Paint or varnish the rudder to match the boat.

For general purposes the boat may be rigged as a gunter sloop (photo 23). For racing it may have the Bermudan sloop rig described later.

A gunter sail has a gaff which is hoisted on the aft side of the mast and extends vertically, or nearly so, above the top of the mast. This gives a sail almost as efficient as the Bermudan, with the advantage of having spars which are all short enough to stow inside the boat. The gunter rig for this boat has a total area of about 66 sq. ft. (fig. 32, 1).

The mast, gaff and boom are all solid round spars, preferably made of spruce. Gaff and boom are parallel in the length, but the mast is tapered. Make these parts as described in Chapter 6. At the top of the mast make two chocks to support the shrouds and forestay. They should be a hard wood, such as oak, and securely screwed

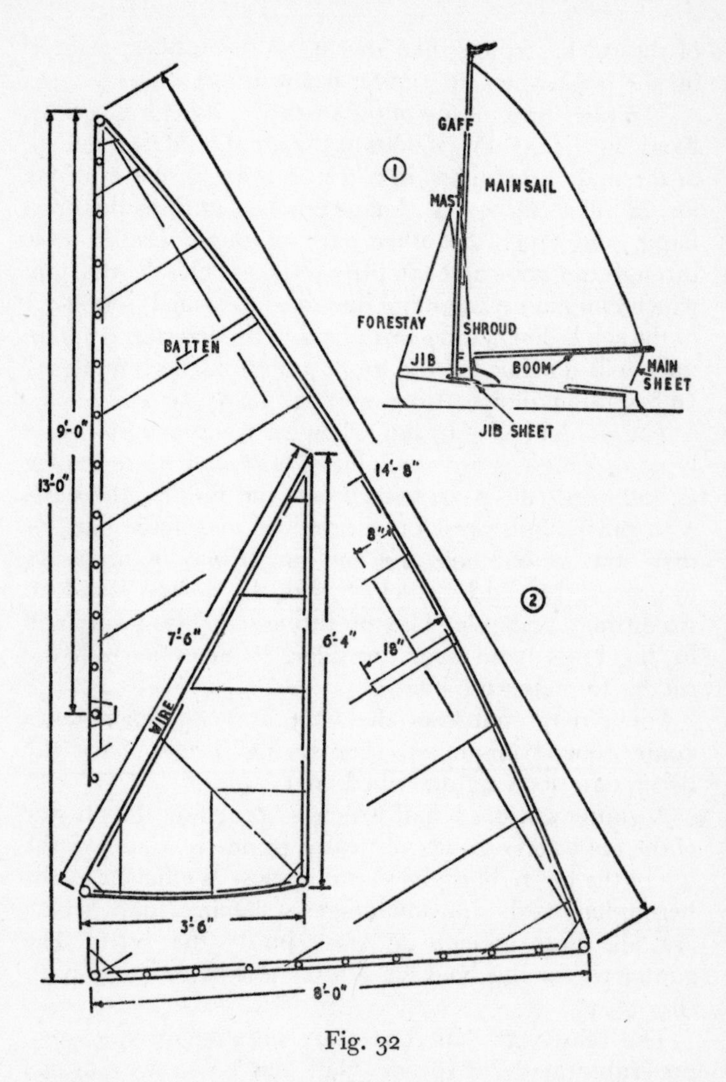

Fig. 32

and glued (fig. 33, 1) as the strain on them may be considerable. Let in a sheave for the main halliard (fig. 33, 2). Drill holes for the ends of the slot, with an assistant sighting endwise to see that you are going through correctly.

Join the holes with pencil lines on each side then remove some of the waste by drilling other holes part way from each side. Use a chisel to open out the slot, and finish its sides with a file. Drill a hole for a rod which forms the axle for the sheave. A small block is needed just below this on the forward side to take the jib halliard (fig. 33, 3). Arrange a cleat each side of the mast to take the halliards. The foot of the mast has a tenon to fit the mast step. It is better for the thrust to be taken on the top of the step by the part surrounding the tenon than to have the tenon so long that its end takes the weight.

The lower end of the gaff has jaws made by screwing on plywood cheeks (fig. 33, 4). They should be spaced wide enough to slide easily on the mast. To prevent them jumping off a line can be fastened through holes. The simplest way to attach the halliard is to drill a hole through the gaff (fig. 33, 5). This brings the gaff close up to the mast. To strengthen the gaff, strips may be fixed each side of the hole. Drill holes near the ends to take the lashings for the sail.

The boom has a hole for lashings at each end and it pivots on the mast with a gooseneck. The gooseneck is a universal joint and several versions are made. The simplest has a fixed bracket on the mast and the hinge part driven into the end of the boom. A better type has a track on the mast (photo 26). This allows the sail to be tensioned by pulling the boom down after hoisting.

It is advisable to make a trial assembly with the sail before dismantling and remove fittings before varnishing the spars.

The mast is supported by three stays—one to the stem, called a forestay, and one each side to points just forward of the rowlock swells, called shrouds. The two shrouds may be in a continuous length. Use ring plates (fig. 34, 1) or shroud plates (fig. 34, 2) at all three points. It is possible to use fibre rope for the stays, but it is better to use flexible wire rope. The expert might splice the wire, but clips are

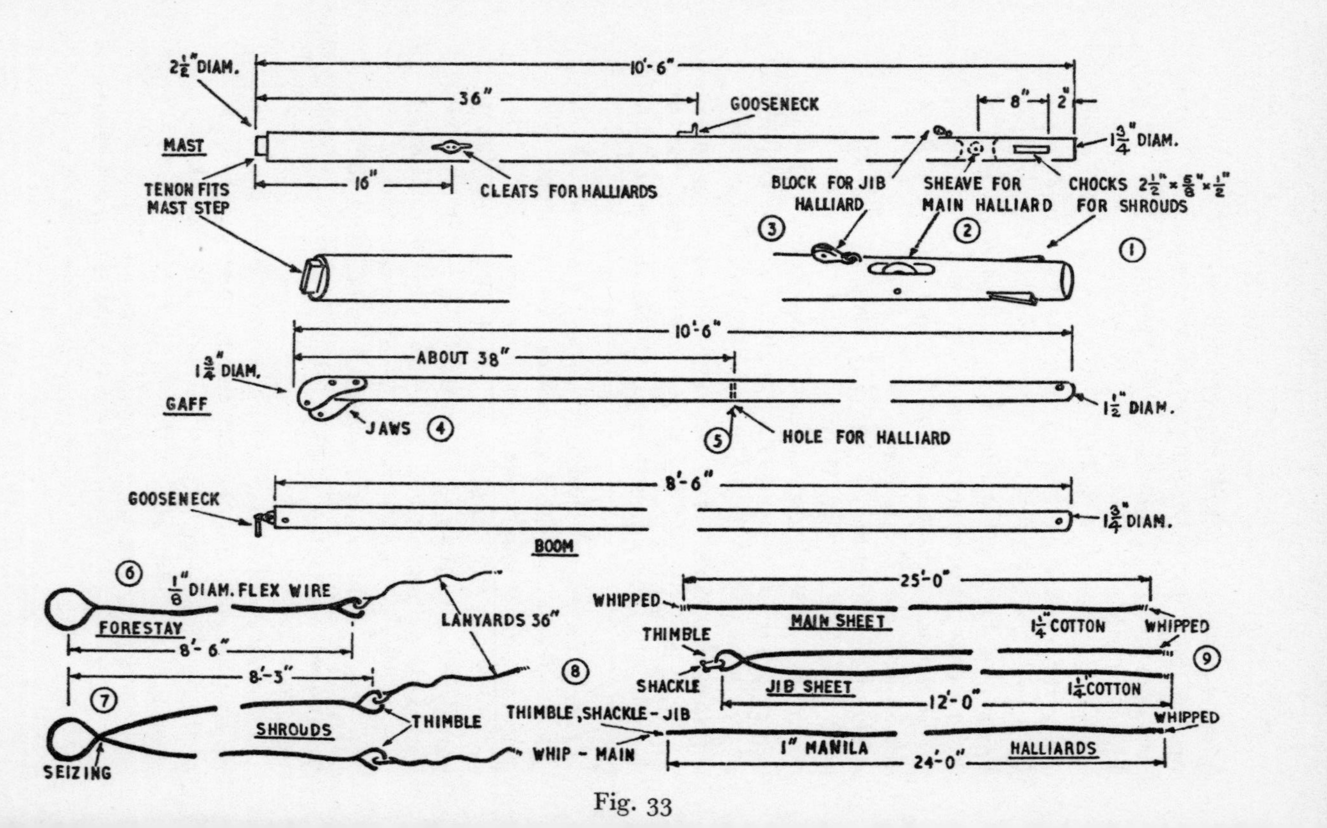

2½" DIAM.
10'-6"
36"
GOOSENECK
8"
2"
MAST
1¾" DIAM.
TENON FITS MAST STEP
16"
CLEATS FOR HALLIARDS
BLOCK FOR JIB HALLIARD
SHEAVE FOR MAIN HALLIARD
CHOCKS 2½" × ⅝" × ½" FOR SHROUDS
3
2
1
10'-6"
ABOUT 38"
1¾" DIAM.
GAFF
JAWS
4
5
HOLE FOR HALLIARD
1½" DIAM.
8'-6"
GOOSENECK
1¾" DIAM.
BOOM
6
⅛" DIAM. FLEX WIRE
FORESTAY
LANYARDS 36"
8'-6"
8'-3"
8
7
SHROUDS
THIMBLE
SEIZING
WHIP - MAIN
THIMBLE, SHACKLE - JIB
25'-0"
WHIPPED
MAIN SHEET
1¼" COTTON
WHIPPED
THIMBLE
SHACKLE
JIB SHEET
1¼" COTTON
9
12'-0"
WHIPPED
1" MANILA
HALLIARDS
24'-0"

Fig. 33

available and the best ends are spliced by a patent method with equipment most chandlers have available. Having the ends finished in this way does not add much to the cost of the wire.

The approximate lengths of the stays are given, but they should be checked on the actual boat. The lower ends should come 6 in.–9 in. from the eyes to which they are fixed. The forestay (fig. 33, 6) has a loop to fit over the mast and a thimble spliced at the lower end with a fibre rope lanyard. The shrouds may be made separately like the forestay, or in one length (fig. 33, 7 and 34, 6) with a loop to fit over the mast held by a seizing. The stays are tensioned by taking several turns with the lanyards and finishing with a clove hitch (fig. 34, 3).

The two halliards are plain pieces of whipped rope, although rigging is simplified if the jib halliard has a thimble and shackle at one end (fig. 33, 8).

The jib sheet has two parts, with a thimble and shackle for attaching to the sail (fig. 33, 9). In use the sheet is brought aft at each side of the boat and the best set of the sail is obtained if the parts are led through thimbles at each gunwale (fig. 34, 4). The thimbles are in short lines which go through drilled holes and fasten to the risers.

The main sheet is given a two-to-one purchase. An eyeplate is fixed at one side of the opening in the transom and a small block at the other side (fig. 34, 5). A screw eye may be forced open to take the becket of the block. On the boom there is a rope strop holding another block. A knotted end of the main sheet is held by the eyeplate. The sheet goes up to the block on the strop, then through the block on the transom to the helmsman's hand.

The sails (fig. 32, 2) may be bought. Several British sailmakers have the drawings, or the drawings in this book provide sufficient information for them to work from. Alternatively, if the reader wishes to make his own sails, he will find it an interesting job which calls for care and patience rather than a high degree of skill. Detailed

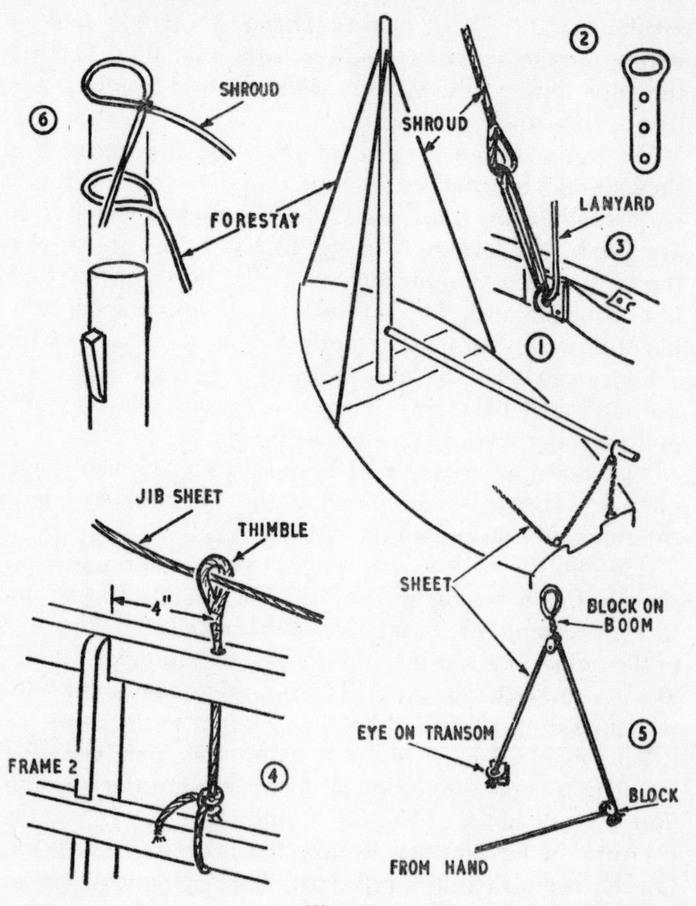

Fig. 34

instructions are given in the book *Make your own sails* by Bowker and Budd, published by John Murray.

The jib has eyelets at the corners. There are hanks on the luff to attach it to the forestay. The shackle on the jib halliard engages with the eyelet at the peak. A short length of line serves as a lanyard from the tack to the forestay fitting and the jib sheet shackles to the eyelet at the clew. The two straight edges of the main sail have eyelets. The large eyelets are used to stretch the sail along its spars, with several turns of light line through the end holes and around the spars. The intermediate eyelets are used with line half-hitched along the spars (fig. 20 G). The eyelets between the jaws of the gaff and the gooseneck may be used to take a line around the mast, if desired. Two wood or plastic battens in pockets keep the roach of the sail extended.

If a pennant is used, it should be attached to a short shaft and lashed so as to extend above the top of the gaff.

Do not strain a new sail too tightly and use it only in light airs at first. It is advisable to leave the locating of the hole in the gaff for the halliard until the first trial assembly, to allow for slight variations.

Chapter 10

WENSUM— 11 FT. DOUBLE-CHINE SAILING DINGHY

Sailing gear—Bermudan rig

THE standard gunter rig as described in Chapter 9 gives a good performance and has been used in some clubs for racing, but the hull is capable of carrying a larger spread of canvas if racing is the main purpose of the boat. The gunter-rigged boat is primarily a general-purpose dinghy, from which the sailing gear may be completely removed, leaving a craft which can be rowed by two, if required, and in which a considerable amount of gear can be stowed. Although any small boat may be capsized, the normal gunter rig on Wensum is very unlikely to bring that problem in normal winds and when handled with commonsense. A boat built as a racing machine carries more sail and therefore has a greater risk of capsizing. Consequently, it is usual to give a racing boat some decking and to carry reserve buoyancy; then most of the water is kept out if the boat heels excessively, and if it does go over the reserve buoyancy makes it float fairly high and bailing is a fairly simple matter.

Nearly all modern racing craft have Bermudan rigs. This means having a mast much longer than the length of the boat, with complications of staying to keep it upright and more of a problem of stowage when the boat is trailed or put in a shed. For a boat which is kept afloat, there is also the problem of stability on moorings. Choppy seas and strong winds could capsize a moored boat which becomes unstable due to the height and weight of the mast.

If the boat is to be a racer it cannot also be regarded as

WENSUM

11 FT. DOUBLE-CHINE SAILING DINGHY

Material Schedule

(variations on the standard schedule given in Chapter 9)

Omit items K, L and M. Reduce the lengths of risers (F) to 3 ft.

Add the following items:

Part	*Name*	*Number required*	*Length ft.*	*Length in.*	*Width in.*	*Thickness in.*	*Wood*
Q	Mast box	2	2	0	4¼	⅞	M
–	Mast box	2	2	0	3	⅞	M
R	Deck beam	1	4	0	3⅞	⅞	M
S	King plank	1	3	2	5⅞	⅞	D
T	Carlins	2	8	0	1⅜	¾	M
U	Coaming	2	2	4	3	½	M
	Boom	2	8	6	2	¾	S
	Mast	2	18	0	2¾	1⅛	S

Skin and decks—the hull may be covered with ¼ in. plywood as described for the standard boat, or reduced to 4 or 5 mm. for lightness. Most of the decking may be made from offcuts from the hull or made from 1 piece 4 ft. wide and 3 ft. 2 in. long, and 1 piece 8 ft. × 2 ft.

Fittings are mostly the same as for the standard rig, but variations are described in the chapter.

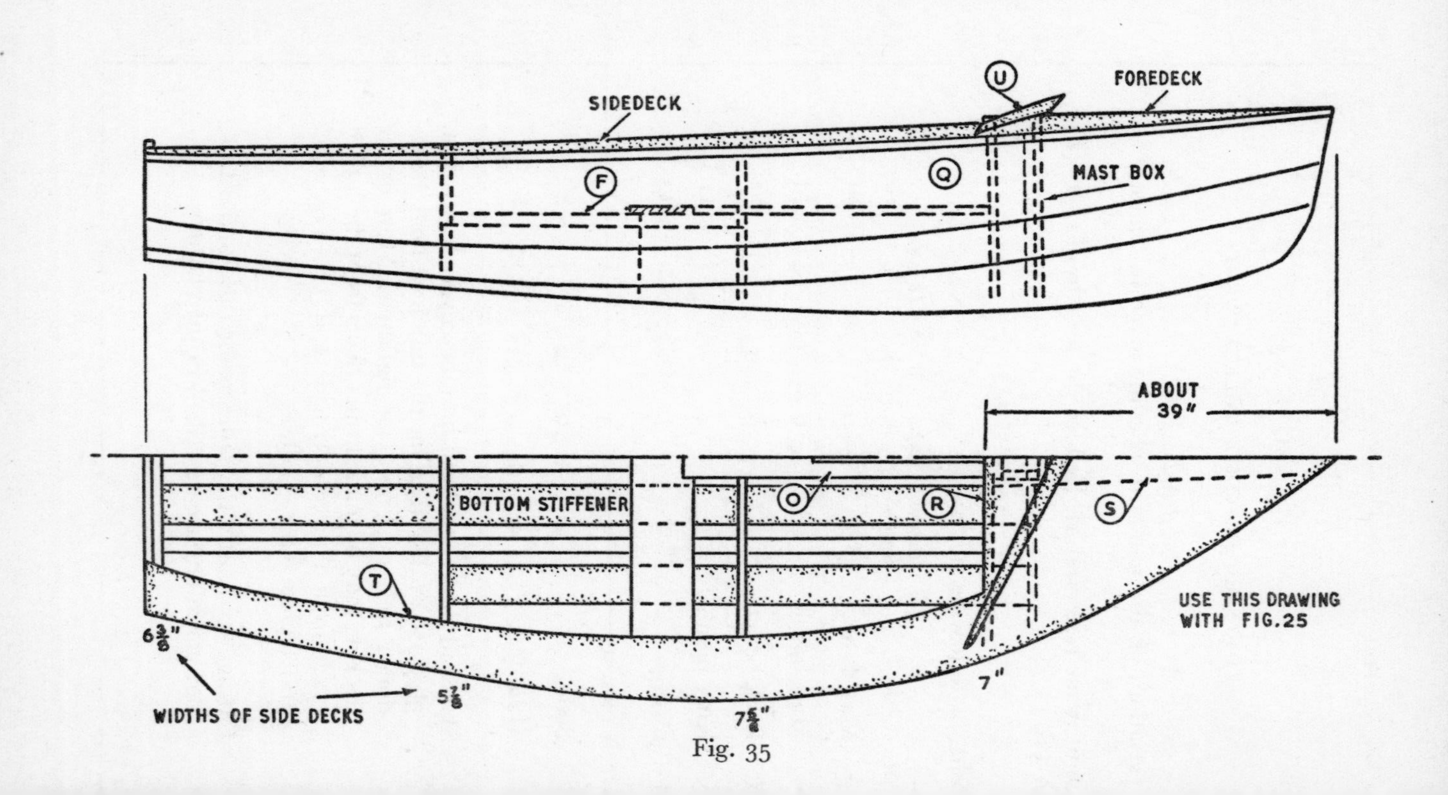

U
FOREDECK
SIDEDECK
Q
MAST BOX
F
ABOUT
39"
O
R
S
BOTTOM STIFFENER
T
USE THIS DRAWING
WITH FIG.25
6 3/8"
5 7/8"
7"
7 5/8"
WIDTHS OF SIDE DECKS

Fig. 35

a general-purpose boat. The decking restricts accommodation and only permits rowing in one position. It is still possible to use an outboard motor. Storage of the mast when the boat is out of use must also be considered.

To rig Wensum as a racer with a Bermudan main sail does not involve any major alterations to the boat; in fact, it is possible to build the boat for rowing only, or rig it with a gunter sail, and adapt it to Bermudan afterwards. However, it is simpler to build with this rig from scratch, if that is the ultimate intention. The main differences are: the bottom boards are removed and the bottom itself is stiffened at important points; there is only one thwart (parts K, L, M omitted); although the mast is in the same position, it fits into a box which also supports the forward end of the centre-board case; there is a foredeck coming aft of the mast and full-length side decks (fig. 35). The rudder and centreboard are the same as described for use with the simpler rig.

Construction is the same as described in Chapters 8 and 9 in all major respects. The hull is the same up to the stage when it is turned over. The riser (F) need only come between frames 2 and 3. There will be no need to fit knees or breasthook, as the decking serves to stiffen these joints.

Make and fit the thwart (J) and the centre-board casing, with the gangboard (O), except that the forward end of the gangboard finishes flush with the end of the case. Make the aft part of the mast box (Q) (fig. 36, 1) and screw and glue it to the forward end of the centre-board case. The deck beam (R) comes immediately aft of it. Mark where it comes on the gunwales and make the beam to fit, with its lower edge flush with the undersides of the gunwales. Curve the top so that it rises about $2\frac{1}{4}$ in. at the centre. Fix it to blocks on the gunwales. Make up the other sides of the box. At the bottom thicken the frame joint cover and put a piece inside to support the mast foot, but leave a space so that water can drain through (fig.

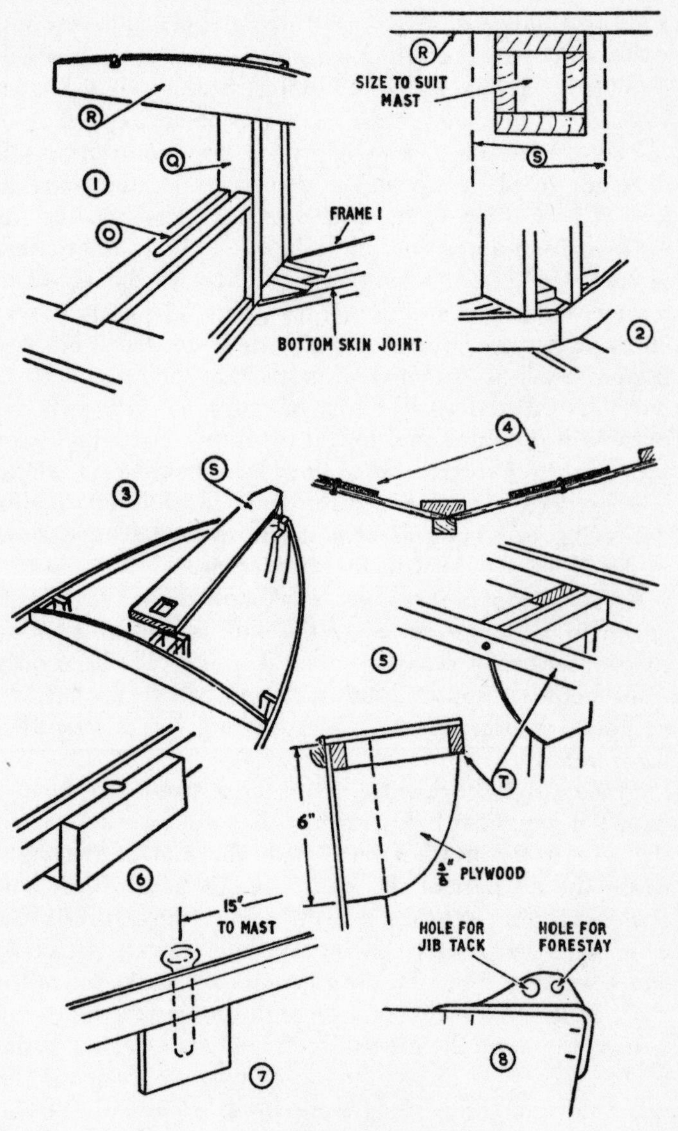
R
Q
1
O
FRAME I
BOTTOM SKIN JOINT
R
SIZE TO SUIT
MAST
S
2
S
3
4
5
T
6"
$\frac{3}{8}$" PLYWOOD
6
15"
TO MAST
7
HOLE FOR
JIB TACK
HOLE FOR
FORESTAY
8

Fig. 36

36, 2). A king plank (S) fits between the beam and the stem, which must be notched to take it (fig. 36, 3). Cut the top of the box to fit under the king plank and make a hole to take the mast.

It is advisable to fix the bottom stiffening before completing the deck. This consists of strips of plywood, the same thickness as the hull, about 4½ in. wide: four between frames 1 and 2, and 2 and 3; then two between frame 3 and the transom, arranged centrally in the spaces. They should be glued down and may be held by a row of ¾ in. brass nails at about 3 in. intervals along their centrelines, driving through and clenched (figs. 35 and 36, 4).

The side decking is supported by carlins (T). These are notched into the deck beam (R) and the framing of the transom. The curve of the top of the transom should be reduced slightly so that when sighted it is approximately the same as that of the deck beam. Intermediately, the carlins are supported by plywood brackets with thickened tops (fig. 36, 5). Assemble all the deck framing. Put blocks aft of the deck beam to act as deck joint covers. Fair off the top surfaces thoroughly (photo 24).

If the boat is to be equipped for rowing, thicken the gunwales about 12 in. aft of the edge of the thwart (fig. 36, 6). Stiffen the skin below the gunwales to take the strain of the shroud plates (fig. 36, 7).

The decking is made of the same plywood as the hull. The foredeck may be one piece, or it may be made from two pieces with a joint along the centre of the king plank. The side decks may each be made in one length, or there can be joints on either or both frames. Offcuts from the hull may be used up in this way.

Fit the foredeck first. Use glue and brass nails at about 2 in. intervals. Work back from the foredeck when fixing the side decks, bedding the joints well in glue. Level the edges of the plywood. Cover the outside joint with a piece of half-round moulding (I). The shroud plates go outside the skin and the moulding should be notched around them.

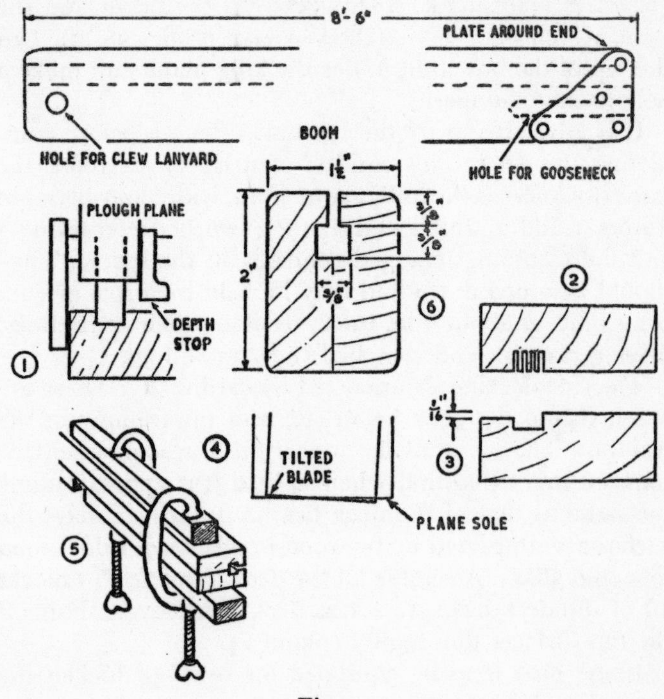

Fig. 37

At the stem, the neatest fitting for the forestay and the tack of the jib is a piece which goes over the stem (fig. 36, 8), although an eye plate or another shroud plate could be adapted. A coaming (U) on the aft side of the foredeck will prevent water running on board (photo 25).

It is usual in Bermudan-rigged small boats for the roped edge of the sail to fit into grooves in the mast and the boom. The alternative is to fit a track on the mast and slides on the sail, and to either fix to the boom in the same way, or to lace the sail as described for the gunter rig. To permit easy grooving, it is usual to make the spars in two parts glued together. This also has the effect of minimizing any tendency to warp, as the grains of the two pieces

16. Corrib: the hull immediately after turning over.

17. Corrib: painting the boat. Note the bottom boards in the background.

18. Wensum—the framework, viewed from forward.

19. Wensum.

resist each other's attempts to distort. Besides the sail grooves, some masts are also lightened by hollowing before glueing up. It is possible then to carry halliards down through the mast and reduce windage. The mast for Wensum could be hollowed, but it is shown as solid as this requires less skill to make. It is advisable to tackle the boom first to gain experience in the work.

For the boom see that the two parts match each other and are reasonably straight. There are several ways of making the groove. A craftsman using hand methods does the job with a plough plane. This has a blade of the right width and gauges to regulate depth and distance from the edge (fig. 37, 1). With a small circular saw, such as may be driven by an electric drill, the groove may be cut by making a series of saw cuts to remove most of the waste (fig. 37, 2) then the groove pared and scraped clean with a chisel. Some circular saws may be fitted with a wobble device so that the saw can be adjusted to make a groove of the required width in one cut. The groove may be left with a square bottom, or a hollow plane can be used to round it. In any case, all roughness should be removed with glasspaper. To allow for the thickness of the sail cloth about $\frac{1}{16}$ in. should be taken off each edge beside the groove (fig. 37, 3). This may be done with a rebate plane or a fillister (a rebate plane with an edge gauge), or with an ordinary plane in which the blade has been adjusted so as to cut on the edge (fig. 37, 4).

Glue the two parts of the boom. The job should be cramped, but excessive pressure is unnecessary. Local pressure should be avoided, and this is best done by using long strips of fairly stout wood under the cramps (fig. 37, 5). Although sufficient glue should be used, avoid getting an excess squeezing into the groove, which may be difficult to remove. The boom finishes parallel throughout its length and is merely rounded on the corners (fig. 37, 6).

The mast is grooved in a similar way, except that the

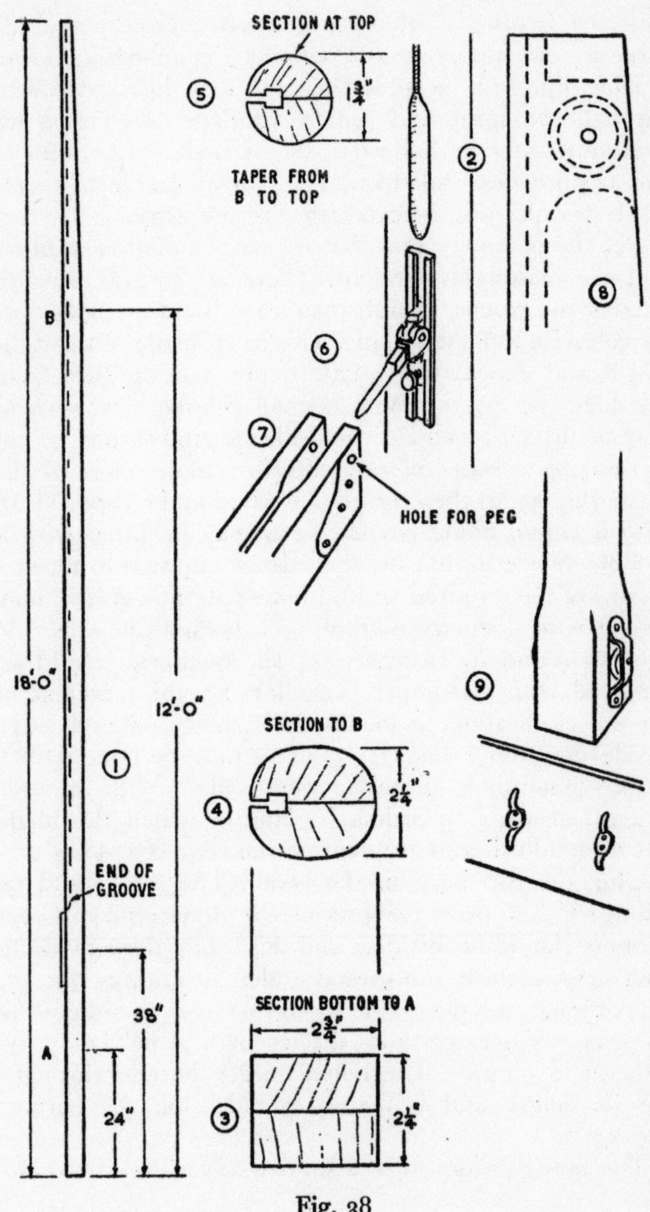
SECTION AT TOP
5
$1\frac{3}{4}$"
TAPER FROM
B TO TOP
2
8
B
6
7
HOLE FOR PEG
18'-0"
12'-0"
9
SECTION TO B
1
4
$2\frac{1}{4}$"
END OF
GROOVE
38"
SECTION BOTTOM TO A
$2\frac{3}{4}$"
A
24"
3
$2\frac{1}{4}$"

Fig. 38

groove stops above where the boom is attached (fig. 38, 1). Also at this point the groove is widened so that the head of the sail can be admitted and fed in as the sail is hoisted (fig. 38, 2). When the two parts have been glued up the outside has to be shaped. From the foot of the mast to above deck level the section is rectangular (fig. 38, 3). From here to the point where the shrouds and forestay are attached the wood is made to a parallel elliptical section (fig. 38, 4). The extreme top of the mast is round and the section tapers to this (fig. 38, 5), but all of the taper is from the front and sides, leaving the aft side straight.

Plane the taper at the top first, in rectangular section, then take off the corners in a similar way to that described for the gunter rig. The work is eased if the mast can be supported full-length by a bench or plank, but if only partial support is possible be careful of getting uneven shaping. Sight along the spar frequently to see that the planing is not having a wavy effect in the length. When the spar has been brought to an approximate shape by planing, finish by work around the spar with glasspaper, then work along the grain.

The boom is best attached to the mast with a gooseneck fitting. This is a universal joint, permitting the boom to swing in all directions. Several types are possible, but for this rig one consisting of a spiked piece to fit in the boom and a short track on the mast is convenient (fig. 38, 6). A plate with a square hole fits on the boom (photo 26). The boom can be pulled aft to release the square part of the spike and the sail rolled around the boom to reef it. At the tack of the sail there may be an eye or grommet through which a peg may pass through the boom. A short length of the groove should be opened out at this end (fig. 38, 7). At the other end a short lanyard on the sail may go to a hole through the boom to tension the foot of the sail.

Let a sheave into the mast near the top for the main

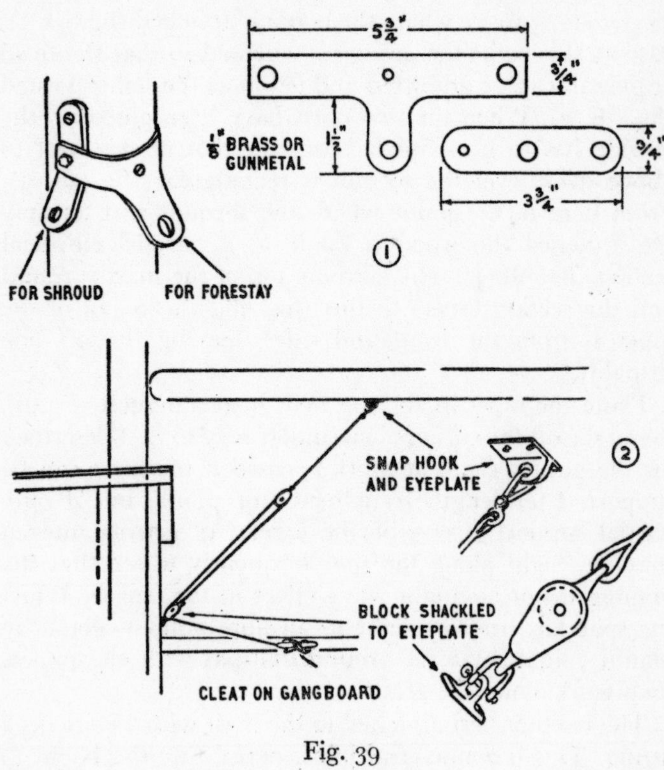

Fig. 39

halliard (fig. 38, 8). This and the jib halliard can be brought down to cleats at each side of the mast above the deck, or taken through sheaves on the side of the mast to cleats on the deck beam (fig. 38, 9).

The shrouds and forestay cannot be taken around the mast, as that would interfere with hoisting the sail. Instead there has to be a fitting about three-quarters of the way around the foreside of the mast. It is possible to buy stainless steel and other fittings for this purpose, but a simple type which can be made from sheet brass is shown (fig. 39, 1).

The forestay and shrouds should be made of galvanized

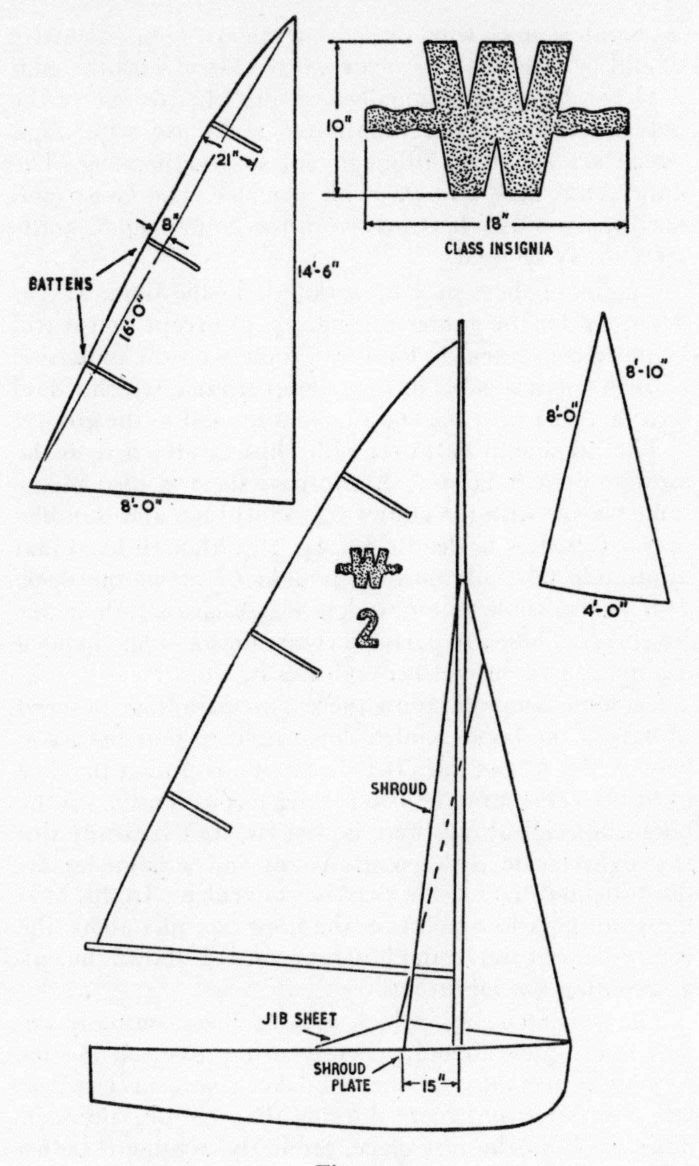
10"
18"
CLASS INSIGNIA
21"
8"
BATTENS
16'-0"
14'-6"
8'-0"
8'-10"
8'-0"
4'-0"
W
2
SHROUD
JIB SHEET
SHROUD
PLATE
15"

Fig. 40

or stainless steel wire—19-strand about $\frac{3}{32}$ in. diameter should be suitable. The neatest way to deal with the ends is to get them professionally eye-spliced with one of the patent methods. The alternative is to use wire clips, which are effective, although not so good-looking. The upper ends may be fixed with shackles. The lower ends may be fixed with lanyards, as in the gunter rig, or bottle screws may be used.

The main sheet may be arranged in the same way as described for the gunter rig (fig. 34, 5) except that it will be more convenient to have an eyeplate on the underside of the boom instead of having a loop around, which would have to come near the end to avoid the sail in the groove.

The jib should be fitted with clips to attach it to the forestay as it is hoisted. A two-part sheet is used in the same way as with the gunter rig. Short lines and thimbles may be used as fairleads (fig. 34, 4), although fixed and adjustable fairleads may be bought to fit on the deck. It is also possible to buy quick-release cleats to hold the jib sheets. These are particularly useful for single-handed sailing. A jerk on the sheet releases it.

On some points of sailing there is an advantage in speed in having the boom hauled down tight so that the sail is kept as flat as possible. It is becoming common practice to fit a kicking strap or boom vang to put tension on the boom. Special fittings may be bought, but basically this is a light tackle between the boom and a point as low down behind the mast as may be convenient. In this boat the strap goes to a point on the mast box just above the centre-board case. A simple arrangement is shown (fig. 39, 2) avoiding special fittings.

The sails for a boat which is to be raced seriously are best made professionally. The drawing gives all the information necessary for the sailmaker (fig. 40). Terylene sails are faster and more durable than cotton, although more costly in the first place. Similarly, rigging is better in Terylene than in natural fibre ropes.

The insignia shown is the special one for the class and should be sewn on both sides of the sail (photo 27). White sails have black insignias, but on dark coloured sails white markings may be preferable. For identification of individual boats of the class sail numbers may be registered, and a number should be applied for before a sail is made. Details of registration may be obtained from the author (see Preface).

Although this Bermudan-rigged version of the Wensum would not sink if capsized or filled, it would be difficult to right it and bale while it floated almost awash. To make it float higher and support the crew air bags should be fitted. A triangular bag occupying most of the space under the foredeck may be balanced by a cylindrical one across the transom. Makers supply sets of bags for boats of various sizes and a set to suit an 11 ft. boat will be found to fit. It is unwise to sail this or any other racing dinghy without reserve buoyancy firmly fixed in the boat.

It is usual to fly a small racing flag at the top of the mast. Its presence indicates that you are racing and it also serves as a guide to the direction of the apparent wind. Some owners fix it permanently to the mast, but as you should lower it if you withdraw from a race it is better to have it on a short stick which is hoisted by a halliard of light line.

Chapter 11

EQUIPMENT

MANY builders of small boats buy all of the equipment. This is quite satisfactory, of course, but anyone who can make a boat, should also be able to make such things as oars and paddles, fenders and other canvas equipment, rigging and other ropework.

Oars may be made of spruce for inland use. These may also be used at sea, but ash oars stand up better to rough use. Traditionally, ash oars are straight-bladed, while spruce oars may be straight-bladed, but are more often spooned. The dense heavy ash does not absorb much water, so ash oars are often left unvarnished, but spruce is very absorbent and oars made from this wood should be kept well-varnished, both to improve appearance and to prevent water being soaked up to increase the weight of the oars.

Ash is a difficult wood to work, as well as being heavy, so for home construction spruce is suggested. Spoon blades are a job for the craftsman, using special tools, but straight-bladed oars can be made with the ordinary tools used to build the boat. The size depends on the beam of the boat —it is easiest to row if the grips almost meet. As an example an oar 6 ft. 6 in. long is described. This suits Wensum, but other sizes may be made in the same way.

Start with a straight piece of spruce, 2 in. square. Sight along it to see that it is straight. At the blade end glue on pieces to make up the width to 5½ in. or 6 in. (fig. 41 A). Use synthetic resin glue. Either use cramps or rope loops with wedges (fig. 41 B). Do not cramp excessively tight or the joints may become starved of glue.

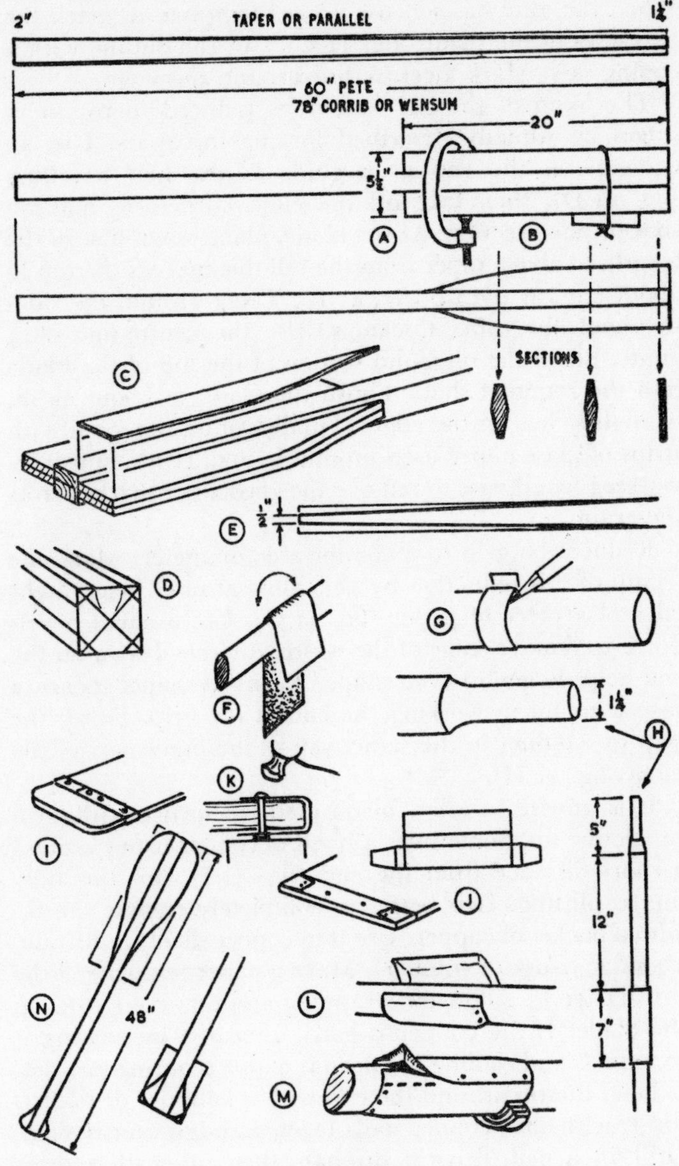
2"
TAPER OR PARALLEL
1¼"
60" PETE
78" CORRIB OR WENSUM
20"
5½"
A
B
SECTIONS
C
½"
E
D
F
G
1¼"
H
K
I
5"
12"
J
7"
L
N
48"
M

Fig. 41

When the glue has set, use a card template to mark the two sides of the blade (fig. 41 C). Cut the outline with a coping saw. Mark a centre-line around this edge.

The loom of the oar has to be reduced to round in stages, as already described for making spars. Use an octagon on the end as a guide to the first bevelling (fig. 41 D), then take off the eight corners to make a sixteen-sided section. At the blade, plane down first in the length, to give a taper from the full thickness at the top to about ½ in. at the tip (fig. 41 E). Taper around the sides to about the same thickness. Use the centre-line as a guide. Blend the diamond section of the top of the blade into the rounded shaft. Finish the blade to about $\frac{7}{16}$ in. or slightly less on the edges. Finally round the loom with strips of glass paper used around it (fig. 41 F). Finish by working lengthwise to remove the glasspaper marks across the grain.

Reduce the grip to a comfortable diameter. Mark the length of this reduction by pencilling around the straight edge of a piece of paper (fig. 41 G). Use a chisel bevel-down to remove some of the waste. A circle drawn on the end helps to get an even shape. A curved shaper tool or a rasp is useful in working the end of the grip. Finish the grip by sanding in the same way as the main part of the loom (fig. 41 H).

It is unwise to use a blade made of spruce without a protective tip. Sometimes a band of copper is put around a short distance from the end (fig. 41 I), but this only limits splitting. It is better to completely enclose the tip with a pocket of copper. Use thin copper sheet (in Britain, about 20 gauge or thinner). Make a paper template of the tip (fig. 41 J). Allow for wrapping around about ¾ in. up the blade. If the copper is hard, anneal it by heating it to redness and cooling it. Clean it with a scouring powder.

Bend the tip around the end with a hammer or mallet. Fix it with thin copper nails taken through and riveted. Drill for a nail, drive it through, then cut it off a short distance above the surface and rivet over the end with light blows while the head is supported by an iron block (fig. 41 K).

Aluminium alloy may be used instead of copper, but it should be a sea-water resistant type. Some aluminium and its alloys corrode rapidly in salt water.

A metal rowlock will soon damage an unprotected spruce oar. It is usual to prevent wear by fitting a leather band. This should be a piece of hide of a size that will extend about 8 in. along the oar and completely encircle it (fig. 41 L). Shave away the under side of the hide at the ends and where it will overlap. This can be done with a sharp knife or razor blade. Soak the leather in water to make it pliable, then bend it around the oar. Fix it with copper tacks, starting from the side opposite to the joint so as to get the edges tight.

Oars are often used with plain leathers, but it is a help in locating them to have buttons. These come against the rowlocks and prevent the metal going over the edge of the leather. If a button is to be fitted, do not shave away the leather band at the top end. Make the button from several thicknesses of leather and fix them with long copper nails. The button should come on the side towards which the oar will be pulled. Have the joint in the leather in line with the centre of one side of the blade and the button on the opposite side (fig. 41 M).

Oars are rather large things to stow when sailing. They are necessary if you expect to have to propel the boat far by your own efforts, but if your main interest is in sailing and you are only likely to need to propel the boat a short distance to the bank, a paddle may be carried instead of oars. This can be made in the same way, but shaped like a small Canadian canoe paddle (fig. 41 N). Round the tip of the blade and build up the other end to form a grip. A boathook shaft may be made by converting a square strip to round. Finish oars and paddles with at least three coats of varnish.

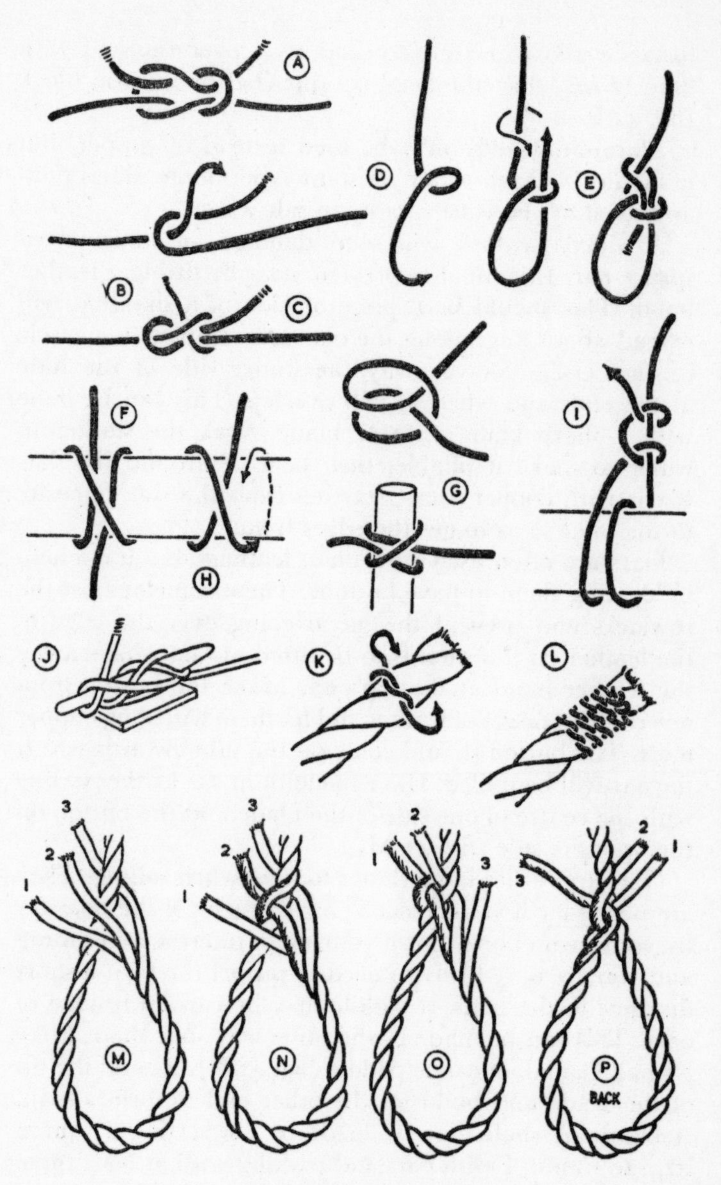

Fig. 42

Anyone who claims to be a proficient boatman should be able to make a few essential knots, whip rope's ends and make an eye splice. The knot that everyone claims to know, but does not always make is the reef knot (fig. 42 A). In this the two parts are twisted together the opposite way the second time. If both twists are made the same way, the result is a granny knot, which is useless. The reef knot is only used when it bears against something. If the knot is in mid-air, it should be a sheet, or common, bend (fig. 42 B). If the ropes are of two different thicknesses, the thicker one is the one around which the other is worked (fig. 42 C).

The only worthwhile knot for making a firm loop is a bowline. There are quick ways of making this, but the basic way for learning is to form a little loop far enough from the end to allow for making the main loop (fig. 42 D). Bring the end up through this, around the standing part and down through the little loop (fig. 42 E). Pull tight by pulling the standing part in one direction and the sides of the loop with the end in the opposite direction.

A clove hitch (fig. 42 F) is commonly used for fastening a rope to a spar or ring. If the end of the spar is available, two loops may be dropped over (fig. 42 G). If not, the working end is taken around, over the standing part and under itself (fig. 42 H). A better knot for the end of a rope is a round turn and two half hitches. The end completely encircles the spar and is used to make a clove hitch around the standing part (fig. 42 I). A clove hitch is a jamming form of two half hitches. A half hitch has many uses on a boat. The last turn around a cleat may be turned back on itself as a half hitch to lock it (fig. 42 J).

An untreated rope's end will soon unravel and be wasted. Synthetic rope may be sealed by heating. Holding a match under the end will soften the filaments so that they melt and run together. Other ropes need whippings. There are many varieties. One of the simplest is the West Country whipping. Use stout thread and prepare it by drawing it through a piece of beeswax or a piece of candle. Put the centre of a length of thread behind the rope, bring the ends forward and knot them together (fig. 42 K). Take them to the back and knot them again. Continue to do this alternately back and front until the whipping is about as long as the thickness of the rope. Pull each knot as tight as possible as it is made. Make the final knot into a reef knot, and cut the ends off (fig. 42 L).

Of the many splices, the one most likely to be needed on a boat is the eye splice. Common rope is three-stranded, with the strands laid up together right-handed, i.e. as you look along the rope the strands twist to the right away from you. To make an eye splice bend the end of the rope into a loop and separate the ends of the strands for a short distance. Arrange the ends, so that two are on the front and one behind. Regard the front as the side where the end strands point across the lay of the rope (fig. 42 M). Tuck the middle end strand under any convenient strand of the standing part of the rope (fig. 42 N). Tuck the end nearer the loop under the next strand, going in where the first comes out (fig. 42,O). Turn the splice over and find the main strand which does not have an end strand under it. Tuck the remaining end strand under this in the same direction as the other two (fig. 42 P). This should leave you with an end strand projecting from each space in the rope. Even up the splice so far, then tuck each end in turn over the adjoining main strand and under the next, aginst the lay. When all three are tucked, do it once more with each end, so that each has been tucked three times. For neatness, about half the fibres in each strand may be cut out and one more tuck made with each strand reduced to half thickness. The whole splice may be rolled between boards to even up its appearance.

Canvaswork is quite easy and an understanding of it allows you to do repairs and make articles for use on board. Canvas is graded by its weight per square yard. Dinghy sail cloth may be about 3 oz. per square yard.

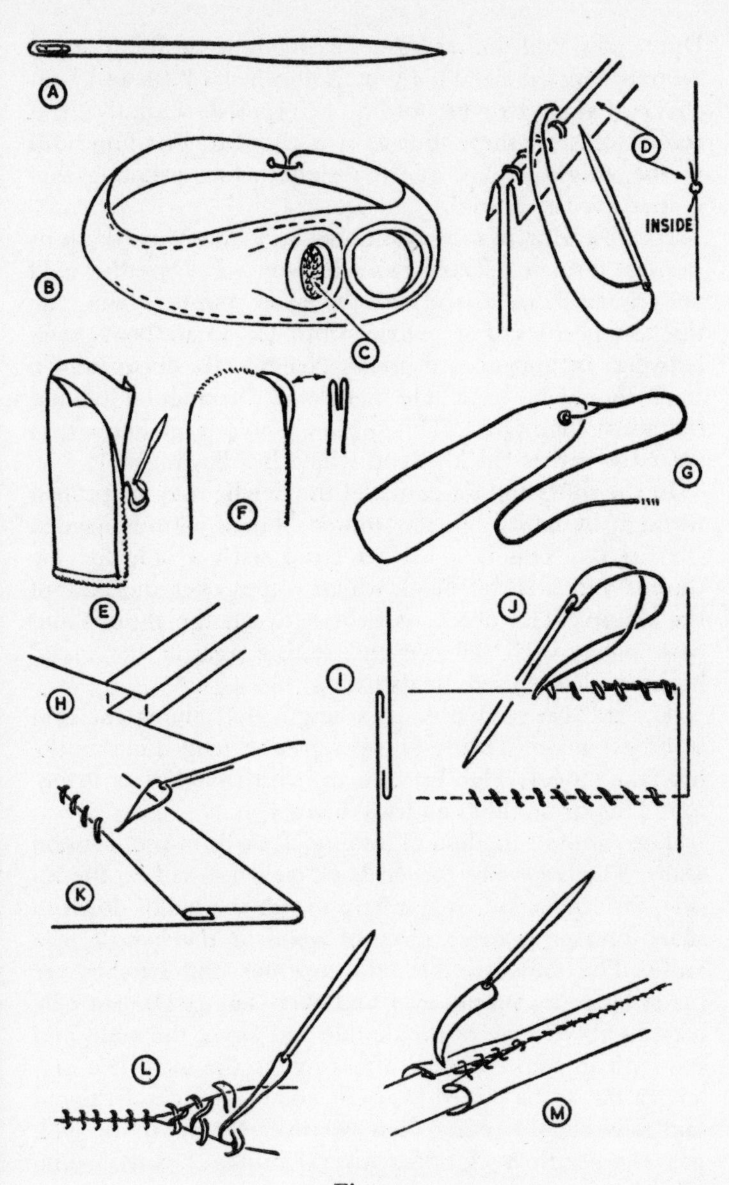

Fig. 43

Duffle bags and similar things are likely to be about 10 oz. Stouter canvas, around 15 oz. is met in kit bags and boat covers. Most canvas to-day is proofed. Usually it is coloured at the same time as it is proofed. Proofing adds to the weight, but it is the weight before proofing that is used for the grade.

Hand sewing of canvas is done with stout thread. In its stoutest form it is known as sail twine. The needles used are graded by numbers, with the lower numbers being the thickest needles. For canvas work for small boats sizes between 15 and 20 are useful. Needles are cheap and a stock should be kept. The needles are triangular behind the point (fig. 43 A). This pushes a hole large enough to clear the rather thick thread which is following.

In the softer lighter canvases the needle may be pushed through by hand, but for stouter cloth a palm is needed (fig. 43 B). This is a leather strap with a hole for the thumb and a metal block which comes over the base of the thumb. The needle is held between the thumb and first finger, with the eye end resting against the metal block, which is used for thrusting (fig. 43 C).

Thread is used double in a length that allows the arm to be extended. Trying to use a greater length makes the job take longer. The thread is drawn through wax before use. This strengthens and waterproofs it.

The simplest method of joining cloths is to use a round seam. The edges are turned back on what will be the inside, for about ½ in. It is a help to rub the bends down to sharp creases, using a piece of wood or the handle of a knife. The folds are brought together and stitches are made by going simply over and over (fig. 43 D). Start by leaving about 1 in. of the double end along the seam and sew over it. Make stitches about five to the inch. If a new length has to be joined in, twist about an inch of the old and new ends together then sew over them. At the end, pass the needle back under several stitches before cutting off.

20. Wensum: the framework, viewed from aft.

21. Wensum: fixing the keel.

22. Wensum: the hull complete, with bottom boards, centre-board and side benches.

23. Wensum: rigged as a gunter sloop, close-hauled in a light breeze.

A round seam can be used in making a fender. Make up a bag inside-out and turn back the edges. Sew along the bottom and up the sides (fig. 43 E). Fill the bag with bits of rope, granulated cork or foam plastic, after turning it the right way. Turn in the top and sew that (fig. 43 F). Fix an eyelet to the top and attach a lanyard with an eye splice. Whip the other end of the lanyard (fig. 43 G).

If pieces of canvas have to be joined to make up the width, as in making a boat cover, the joint is called a flat seam. If the manufactured selvedge is used, the pieces may simply overlap, using the coloured line down the edge as a guide to the amount of overlap (fig. 43 H). If the edges are cut, they should be turned under to prevent fraying (fig. 43 I). Sew along one edge, then turn the job over and sew along the other (fig. 43 J).

If an edge has to be turned in, to strengthen it, to provide a groove for a draw string, or to make a substantial fixing for eyelets, the work is called tabling. The edge is turned under and rubbed down, then sewn in the same way as one side of a flat seam (fig. 43 K).

Another useful stitch is a herringbone. It is used for pulling ripped edges together and for fitting canvas tightly over something. The ends of the thread are knotted together. In a rip the needle is taken up through the far side at the left of the damage, then brought down through the near side and up through the rip on the left of the stitch (fig. 43 L). This is the complete set of actions. After making a stitch the needle goes over it and up through the far side to make the next stitch. Each stitch is pulled tight as it is made. To repair a small rip the stitches may be very close and of varying lengths. No other treatment is needed. For larger damage, the stitches need not be so close, but a patch must be sewn or stuck over the sewing.

If a piece of canvas is to be fitted over something solid, such as a tiller, the edges are turned under and herringboning used to pull the canvas tight (fig. 43 M).

Chapter 12

MAINTENANCE

A SMALL boat which is stored out of the water can be kept serviceable with the minimum of work, particularly if it is stored under cover. A boat kept in a place sheltered from the weather will have the longest life. One stored outdoors in a way which prevents rain and snow settling may not last quite as long, while one kept afloat may still have a useful life, but not as long as the others. Some larger craft are designed to be kept afloat and they only come out for an occasional painting. When clinker boats get old they depend on soaking up water to swell the wood and close the joints. A clinker boat after several seasons' use may leak in an alarming way when launched after being allowed to dry out completely. However, after a week afloat or left where it floats for a few hours on each tide, it will close up and be reasonably tight.

Plywood boats, with their bonding of synthetic resin glue, both between the veneers of the plywood and in the constructional joints, should not leak at all, and they should be tight whether stored afloat, ashore exposed to the weather, or under cover. The only possible enemy when stored ashore is frost. Paint and varnish are not absolutely waterproof. Rain may settle and penetrate the wood. If the boat is left exposed with bare patches, it is an invitation to rain to soak in. In itself, this is not serious, but if the moisture freezes in the wood, due to prolonged frost, the ice formed expands. This may affect the wood, and it will lift the varnish, necessitating cleaning off and re-varnishing.

Boats survive a considerable amount of neglect, but obviously they give less trouble and last longer if looked after. There is nothing wrong with merely turning a boat over and leaving it for a few days between periods of use. However, if it is a place accessible to the public there is the danger of it being used as a seat. Visitors to the waterside seem to regard a boat as the ideal thing on which to perch the family, and this could strain the boat. A boat is designed to take a load when it is supported over a large surface by the water. A small area of skin may not stand up to a heavy local load when ashore. Normally, you should make it a rule to never get into the boat while it is ashore. If it is necessary, be careful to put your feet on structural members, such as frames or hog.

If your boat has a trailer or launching trolley, it may be kept on that. A canvas cover is advisable, and this should be arranged with a slope to shed water. A spar can be used as a ridge pole. For long storage, it is advisable to allow some ventilation to the inside. A cover fixed down tightly will cause stale air inside and this may encourage rot. Lift the cover at each end, in such a way that air can circulate, but rain cannot enter. An alternative is to have the boat upside-down, supported on something a few inches above the ground, so that there is a free circulation of air inside. Put a canvas sheet over the boat, and peg it out like a tent. If the sheet is waterproof a boat stored in this way should keep in as good condition as when stored in a shed.

With large craft there is usually a lengthy fitting-out period each Spring, when everything is overhauled and repainted. With a small boat it is better to do maintenance jobs as they arise, then little has to be done to make the boat serviceable when the weather attracts you out again. If the boat is stored at home, maintenance jobs form an interesting activity during the winter.

With modern varnishes, it is not always necessary or advisable to revarnish every year. Any parts which chafe, should be touched up as needed. If the surface becomes dirty, it may be washed with soap and water. Synthetic detergents will remove dirt, but if any remains it affects the adhesion of subsequent coats of paint or varnish. Paint may last two seasons, but usually, for the sake of appearance, annual painting is customary.

Old paintwork, which is sound, may be cleaned and painted over. Sugar soap, from a paint shop, will remove dirt and leave the surface ready for painting. Follow the directions on the packet. If any gloss remains on the old paint, lightly sand it. It should only be necessary to use a top coat. It is advisable to keep coats of paint to as few as necessary. After the paint has built up, after several seasons, it may crack and blister. The only proper treatment then is to clean it off down to the bare wood and start again.

A professional uses a blowlamp for cleaning off much of the paint, but in unskilled hands this can do a lot of damage, particularly on the varied shapes inside the boat, where the flame may char a projection while your attention is on something beside it. It is better to use a chemical stripper. There are several available which are not dangerous to clothes or skin. They must be washed off afterwards. Their action is to loosen the old paint so that it may be scraped off.

With synthetic resin glues repairs can be made which leave the strength, and usually the appearance, of the boat unharmed. However, they are not suitable for waterside repairs. When cruising, it is advisable to carry some canvas and adhesive to suit. For ordinary proofed canvas, the black reclaim rubber cement is suitable. If the boat is holed, it should be dried and a canvas patch with rounded corners stuck over the damage. For a permanent repair it is usual to glue in a piece of wood.

Small damage may be squared up and a block of solid wood made with a slight taper to push into the hole (fig. 44 A). The hole may be square or diamond shaped.

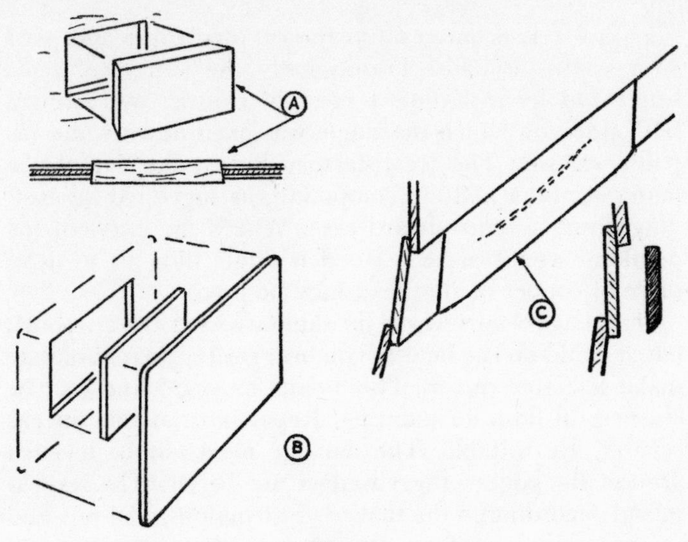

Fig. 44

This should be glued, and the surplus wood outside planed off afterwards. Larger damage may necessitate putting in a piece of plywood of the same thickness as the skin. This should fit the hole and be backed up by another larger piece (fig. 44 B). For a very large repair, the backing piece may have its centre cut out to form a frame, or strips may be mitred around the joint. How the parts are joined depends on their thickness. The glue may be supplemented by screws if the wood is thick enough to take them, nails may be driven through and clenched or riveted over roves. In any case struts will probably have to be arranged inside to force the new pieces to conform to the curve of the original plywood.

Clinker planking is traditionally repaired by tingles if a new length of plank is not scarfed in. Scarfing in a new piece is not easy and is best left to the professional if you are not a craftsman. A tingle consists of a piece of wood shaped to fit over the damage and against the next plank (fig. 44 C). It is faired off at the exposed edges and fixed with screws or nails. Traditionally the joint was made watertight by including a piece of canvas, well-painted both sides, on which the tingle was fixed down while the paint was wet. This is satisfactory, but to-day it might be better to use a jointing compound, as suggested for bedding down a centre-board case. Where the curve of the planking would make a wooden tingle difficult to fit, a piece of copper or thin lead may be used.

If damage occurs where the skin is twisted and a wooden patch could not be bent to conform easily, glass fibre may make a better repair. This bonds to wood and can be cleaned off flush for painting. Repair kits, as sold for car repairs, are suitable. The damage need not be levelled around the edges—ragged edges are better. The resin is mixed according to the maker's instructions, and put into the hole with a reinforcement of glass fibre mat or rovings. Sufficient is put in to stand a little above the final surface, so that it can be sanded off flush when it has hardened. If anything is needed to keep the mixture in place while it sets, polythene sheeting may be put over the hole. Glass fibre makes a very strong and satisfactory repair but care is needed to get proportions correct and to work at above the minimum temperature specified by the makers.

A small boat, particularly if built of plywood, is light enough to be easily transported. It may be carried short distances. Even a 12 ft. dinghy is not too much for four people to carry several hundred yards. However, it is more usual to have a trolley. Launching trolleys are made by several firms and advertised in the yachting magazines. Most of them consist of a pair of small wheels on a long axle with a long looped handle in which the boat rests. The boat is only a few inches above the ground, so the trolley may be wheeled down a ramp or into the water from a beach and the boat floated on or off.

A boat may be sent by rail at a cost based on weight

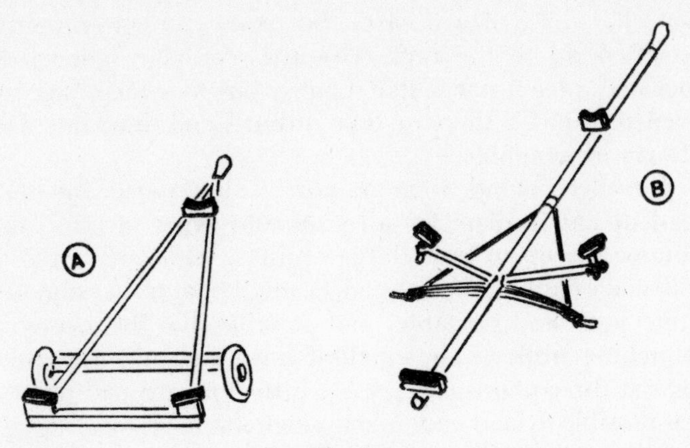

Fig. 45

and distance. Size is not considered, so although the boat may be rather bulky, its transport is not necessarily costly. Sending by passenger train is safer and quicker, but goods train may be cheaper, depending on the rate which the local station want to use. Usually a boat travels better and safer if unwrapped, as the staff can see what it is and they take care of it. Road transport, by general carriers has not been found to be as safe.

A rack on the roof of a modern car will take a surprising load. A boat on the roof does not affect the law regarding the car, providing it is secured properly. A small boat on the roof does not increase the cost of ferrying the car abroad. Handling of the car is very little different from travelling without the load, except that the increased windage may increase petrol consumption and it may be noticable on the steering in a crosswind.

For light craft a roof rack consisting of two crossbars is satisfactory. This rests on pads, which should fit over the curve of the side of the roof and not on the flatter top, and he held down by attachments to the guttering. Heavier craft are better on shaped racks which spread the load over more of the roof. Quite often the governing factor is not what the roof will carry, but what can conveniently be lifted on to the rack with the available labour. A roof may take a particular dinghy, but four men may be needed to put it there or take it down and they may not always be available.

A trailer behind a car is more easily loaded and unloaded, and trailers for all sizes and types of craft are obtainable, up to quite large cruisers, with winches and rollers for hauling the boat on. A small boat trailer may be quite light and portable, and suitable also for use as a launching trolley. The smallest boat may be supported only at three points (fig. 45 A). If the forward pad pivots, it is possible to load and unload single-handed, by bringing the bow on to this pad, then walking around with the stern to drop on the other two pads. The two side pads should be arranged so as to come under the chines. It is wrong to let the weight come on skin panels.

A boat is better supported on its keel. There may be an aft chock as well as a forward one, then the two side chocks are adjustable and merely prevent the boat rocking (fig. 45 B).

In Britain a boat trailer has to conform to a number of regulations, such as have pneumatic tyres, proper springing, mudguards, number plate and brakes if over 2 cwt. There is no additional licence for towing with a private car, but insurance may be affected and there is a speed limit of 30 m.p.h.

Chapter 13

BOAT HANDLING

THERE is a certain something which distinguishes a person with a feeling for boats from one who does not appreciate them and may never have the makings of a seaman. A seaman's first care is for the boat. His every action shows that he takes care of his boat, realising its properties and limitations, knowing what it can and cannot do; appreciating it, often instinctively, as a thing of beauty as well as utility. He keeps it clean and handles it so that it does not become damaged. He takes adequate safety precautions and looks after his boating equipment.

For normal use, any boat should be equipped with at least one painter and there should be a secure fitting to take it at the bow. A second painter at the stern is often useful. How long the painters are depends on circumstances, but they should be longer than the boat in any case, then it can be turned round from the shore without letting go of the lines.

There should be something to take the knocks alongside a wall or dock. There may be a permanent rubber or rope fender around the gunwales, or there may be separate fenders to hang over the side. There should be a bailer—for hard chine boats a flat scoop-type is more use than a rounded one. A cloth for mopping up mud is worth having.

There should be a place for everything, preferably where it can be fixed. A boat hook may have a bracket alongside the centre-board case of a sailing boat. An emergency paddle may be stowed in a rack under the side decks of a runabout or sailing dinghy. If the boat is used for cruising, it may be necessary to take precautions against pilfering. A cupboard with a lock may be built under a thwart. This may take the rowlocks or vital bits from an outboard motor. If there is a foredeck, that may be closed to make a locker with a door. An outboard motor may be secured with a chain and padlock. Oars and boathook may be held to a thwart with chain and padlock so that they cannot be withdrawn above the gunwales (fig. 46 A).

The capable boatman should know what would happen or what he would do in various eventualities. He should take precautions in advance. In a boat, you are more on your own than when called on to deal with some emergencies ashore. If there is a motor or a cooking stove, there should also be a fire extinguisher. There should also be a basic first-aid outfit when cruising or boating for more than just a brief trip.

The most important precaution is against loss of the boat if it capsizes or is holed. A wooden boat may have sufficient inherent buoyancy to support itself just awash, with its crew hanging on to it in the water. A metal or glass fibre hull will not have enough buoyancy and will sink if filled. Although the wooden hull may not sink, it may be difficult to right and salvage if only just awash, so even in this case it is advisable to provide some reserve buoyancy. This is done by building in air compartments in various ways. 1 cubic foot of air will support about 60 pounds. Parts of the hull may be sealed off, or the air may be contained in inflatable bags which should be securely lashed in place. The more reserve buoyancy there is, the higher will the boat float when swamped. Convenient places for buoyancy in a sailing boat are under the foredeck, under side benches or under the stern sheets. If the buoyancy is in the form of fixed compartments, it is usual to provide drain plugs in case they leak slightly.

There are certain buoyant materials which can be built

into a boat. They are mostly foam plastic or rubber and it is the air contained in the little bubbles of the hardened material which give buoyancy. This material may be bought in slabs which can be cut and stuck below decks or anywhere else convenient. It is also possible to form it in position, but at the time of writing this has not been evolved in a satisfactory and economical way for amateur use.

Personal buoyancy is another matter. Everyone who goes afloat in a small boat should be able to swim. The Scout rule of 50 yards in shirt and shorts is a sound one for everyone who wants to go boating. However, the ability to swim is not enough if you capsize a sailing boat. There are things to be done, and if you do not have to worry about how to keep afloat, you can give your attention to them, and maybe get your boat up, bailed and under way unaided.

There are many lifejackets available from yacht chandlers. They may be inflatable by mouth or emergency CO_2 bottle, or there is one ingenious type in which trapped air automatically rises to your shoulders and supports you. There are jackets filled with kapok, which are rather bulky, but there cannot be any fear of their buoyancy being lost through leaks. Cork is too hard and unwieldy for comfortable wear. Besides lifejackets, buoyant cushions are worth having. If the helmsman sits on a kapok cushion he has something immediately handy to throw to anyone in the water.

Clothing will be dictated by the weather. For summer use, the usual outdoor shirt and shorts are correct. When boating it is as well to get resigned to having wet feet occasionally, so old plimsolls are as good as anything. There are some excellent wind and showerproof sailing jackets. Some are available with built-in buoyancy. The sou'wester is probably the best headgear for bad weather, but the traditional peaked yachting cap does not seem to find favour with small boat sailors.

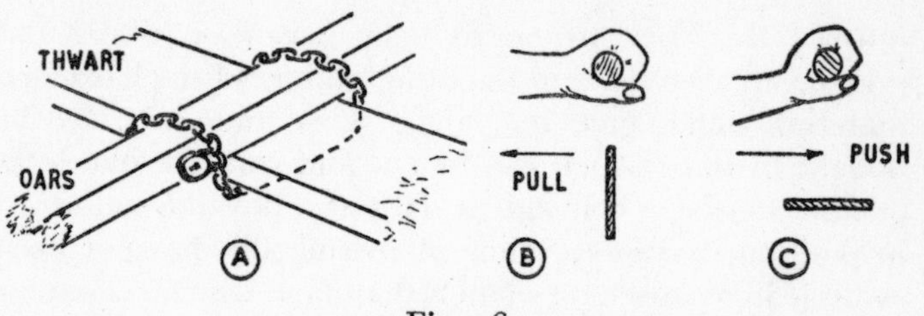

Fig. 46

Even if the boat is to be mainly propelled by sail or power, every boatman should aim to be proficient at rowing and sculling. Names get confused. The racing man says he is rowing if he pulls one oar in a crew with others. He says he is sculling if he pulls a pair of oars. He may call his oars "blades". Some small boat men call their dinghy oars "paddles", but this term is probably better kept for canoe paddles, which may be carried as a reserve means of propulsion in other boats. Sculling, to the seafarer, means using one oar over the stern. What terms you use, depends to a certain extent on local practice—in some places your dinghy will be described as a "punt".

Rowing in a racing boat is a fine art, practised and discussed in great detail, rather like the golfer treats his game, but rowing a small dinghy is not a very complicated process, although practice brings skill. Sit, facing aft, preferably with the feet only slightly bent and braced against something. Have the oars in the rowlocks, held out at right-angles to the boat and with the blades vertical. Lean forward with the arms almost straight and dip the blades in the water. Pull back, keeping the blades at the same depth. At the end of the stroke lift the blades by pushing down the hands. You can now return to the start with the blades in the air.

The beginner often tends to try to row with his arms only. Pull with your body. If you are getting the most power and using the correct action you should find yourself thrusting quite hard on your feet. Swing the whole body backwards and forwards on the seat. Another common fault is lifting the arms too high so that the blades are dipped too deeply. In an extreme case the blade pulls down almost vertical beside the boat and you probably let it slip overboard. A beginner sometimes pulls inboard on the oars towards the end of the stroke. This may lift the oar from the rowlock, pull the wood below the leather over the metal, or cause the ends of the oars to foul each other.

Whether you use long slow strokes or short quick ones depends on you and conditions. Some people work best in "high gear" using short quick pulls. Actually, there is more power to be had for the effort made when the strokes are reasonably long. A short stroke may be completed when the blade is just beginning to exert its greatest thrust. In calm water it is usually best to row with long steady strokes. In choppy water it may only be possible to use much shorter ones.

A refinement is to feather your oars. On the return through the air the blades are parallel with the water. This reduces wind resistance and is less trouble if the blade is hit by a wave. Hold the oars firmly by the grips so that the wrists are straight when the blades are vertical and you are making a normal pull (fig. 46 B). At the end of a stroke, lift the blades from the water by depressing your hands (photo 29). When the blades are in the air, and not before, dip your wrists without releasing your grip on the oars (fig. 46 C). This will turn the blades parallel with the water, and you keep your wrists in the dipped position as you push forward. It is not unnatural and the knack is soon acquired. At the end of the recovery stroke, turn the wrists straight again before dipping the blades in the water. Practice slowly at first. Remember to only alter the angle of your wrists when the blades are in the air.

Steering a dinghy while you are pulling a pair of oars

may seem difficult at first, but as rowing is mastered, steering is done instinctively. Putting more power into one side than the other, without altering the rhythm will correct minor deviations. Pulling only on one side will turn more sharply. An even tighter turn can be made by holding one blade still in the water while pulling with the other. To turn on the spot, pull on one side and backwater on the other. Practice slowly in calm water. Too often a beginner will see that he is about to hit the bank or another boat, and sit there waiting for the collision. It is easy to stop a boat by dropping the blades into the water.

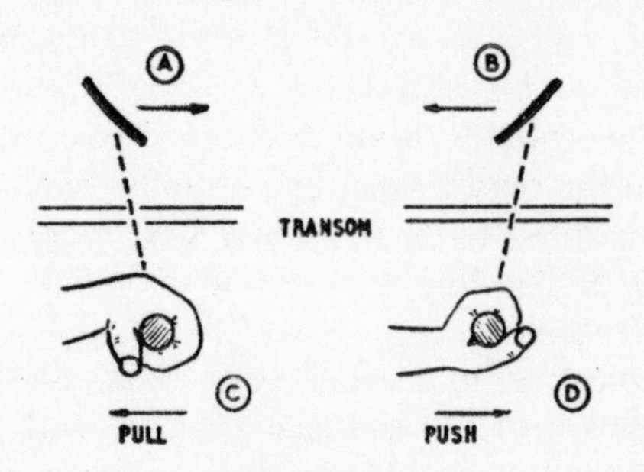

Fig. 47

Holding them vertically may be enough, or they can be backwatered. Most rowlocks have a long arm, against which the oar normally pulls. In backwatering the thrust is against the lower side and care may be needed to avoid lifting the oar out of the rowlock.

After a little practice, an occasional glance over the shoulder will give you a check on the course of the boat. On a long pull a sight of some landmark astern will enable you to keep going in the same direction, once your course has been established. When coming alongside, you let the boat drift the last few yards and control it by letting a blade trail slightly on the side to which you want the boat to turn.

Sculling over the stern is a very worthwhile accomplishment (photo 6). The boat can be propelled and steered at the same time by one oar, working in places where there is insufficient room for normal rowing, and it gives you a second method if one oar breaks or is lost.

The action of sculling is similar in principle to the thrust of a propeller. The blade, at an angle to the travel of the boat, is drawn across (fig. 47 A). The thrust at right-angles to the blade may be resolved into power trying to push the boat forward and power trying to push the stern sideways. If the same angle is used in the opposite direction, the sideways thrust is mostly cancelled out, leaving only the sum of the two forward thrusts (fig. 47 B). As the boat gathers way forward, there is less power lost in the sideways action and more goes towards driving the boat. Actually, sculling over the stern is less mechanically efficient than rowing normally, so it is not a method for going long distances or for use when normal rowing is possible.

The action of sculling makes use of the wrist movement similar to that used for feathering an oar. The difference between the two angles of the blade is about a right-angle, and this is about the amount the wrist can be comfortably moved. When pulling the oar across with the blade at the correct angle, the wrist should be tilted slightly forward (fig. 47 C). At the end of that stroke the wrist is dipped to its normal limit, to turn the blade the other way and a stroke made in the opposite direction (fig. 47 D).

Notice that in sculling correctly the same side of the blade is aft all the time. It is possible to get some sort of drive by using alternate sides, but this is wrong. Although both hands may be needed to get enough power into driving a heavy boat, it is best to only consider the action of one wrist and regard the other hand as merely providing power, rather than control. The greatest power is obtained when the oar is as near vertical as possible. Only the length of the blade should be submerged. As with rowing, long strokes are most effective, but until the boat has been got under way at a reasonable speed, short strokes are needed to avoid excessive yawing. When sculling, the boat may be steered by altering the angle of the blade in one direction, or by pulling harder one way.

An outboard motor may be used on any boat intended for rowing or sailing, but care should be taken to avoid overpowering. This wastes fuel, causes annoyance to others with an excessive wash, and could be dangerous. A runabout designed to plane may be no bigger than a dinghy, but it is designed to rise on to the surface and make use of a powerful motor. A dinghy is designed to go through the water, and a powerful motor on it might push the bow under. Every boat designed to go through the water has an optimum speed—the speed at which it will not go any faster, without using power out of all proportion to the extra speed gained. When it is going at this speed the bow wave is as long as the boat. An observation of this will show you whether the power used is correct. Increasing the power merely pulls the stern down and causes a flurry astern, but progress forward is no better.

Outboard motors are made from fractions of 1 h.p. up to sizes where they cease to be portable power units. Unfortunately, the maker's ratings tend to vary and are not always comparable. An American h.p. is lower than a British one. For small craft, such as those described in this book, a motor less than 4 h.p. should do. Pete does not need more than 1 h.p. Corrib and Wensum can have up to 4 h.p., but for most of the time the motor will be throttled down (photo 30). Motors in this size are mostly single-cylinder two-strokes, with air or water cooling and the fuel tank mounted above the motor. Oil has to be mixed with the petrol and it is important, if the engine is to be trouble-free, that the correct proportions are used. The motor cramps on the transom, and it should have an angle adjustment so that it can be arranged to drive straight forward or slightly upwards (fig. 48 A)—not

24. Wensum: the deck framing faired off ready for the plywood.

25. Wensum: finishing the decked hull.

26. A gooseneck fitting on a slide, with a plate for the end of the boom.

27. Wensum close-hauled, showing the general arrangement of the Bermudan rig.

28. Wensum goir about, showir the arrangemer of sheets. No the air bag in tl stern. The helm man is changir sides, while tl crew prepares haul in the j sheet on tl other tack.

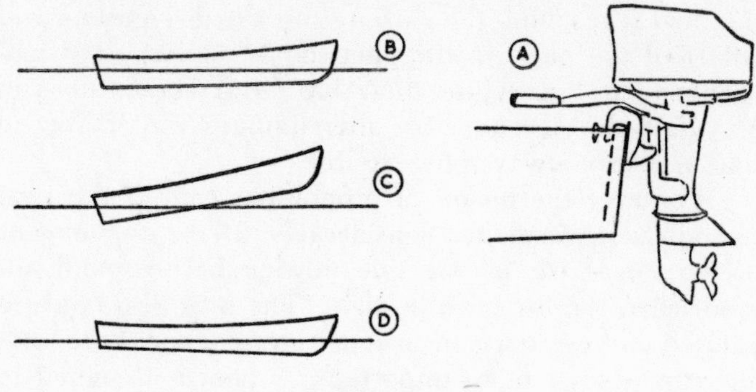

Fig. 48

downwards. Standard motors suit a transom height of not more than 15 in. If the height is more than this the propeller will not be properly submerged. Long-shaft models are made for deeper sterns.

Modern outboard motors are efficient machines if handled according to the maker's instructions. The most common emergencies are fouled plug, fuel stoppage and a sheared pin in the propeller. If something lodges across the points of a sparking plug, it no longer sparks and the engines will not run. If the engine stops or fails to start, this is the first thing to look at. It is always advisable to carry a spare plug and a spanner for it. If there is sufficient fuel in the tank it nearly always gets through, as the filters can take care of a considerable amount of dirt, but they should be removed and cleaned occasionally. To avoid damage to the power unit, propellers are fitted with some kind of weak link which will fail of the propeller hits an obstruction. The most common arrangement is a metal pin through the shaft, transmitting the drive to the propeller. This will break in emergency and has to be replaced. Practice dealing with all of these emergencies before going afloat and carry spares. If starting is by pulling a loose cord, have a spare piece of rope available. If an engine fails to start after a few pulls on the cord, check that fuel is reaching the carburettor. Further pulling will only foul the plug, so the plug should be inspected and changed. In an engine that has been known to run previously and has not been altered in any way, failure to start is nearly always plug trouble.

Whatever the means of propulsion, trim of the boat can affect performance considerably. If the oarsman or his passengers sit to one side, rowing becomes difficult even when the list is quite slight. The boat also tends to follow a curved course instead of a straight one. Fore-and-aft trim is even more important. A boat is designed to float on a level keel—when viewed from the side the stem should be slightly higher than the stern (fig. 48 B). The most important factor affecting speed is the length of the boat—a long boat is faster than a short boat. If all of the weight is in the stern and several feet of keel are in the air at the stem, the boat, in effect, has been shortened (fig. 48 C) and its maximum speed is related to the shorter waterline length. If the boat is down by the bow (fig. 48 D), it will push up a large bow wave, which will slow its progress. Steering also becomes difficult. The effect on speed is particularly noticeable in a sailing boat.

Normally the boat should be loaded so that it floats level. This may mean sitting well forward to control an outboard motor when alone, or arranging passengers suitably, rather than letting them sit where they wish. With a head wind there may be some advantage in having the boat loaded slightly down by the bow and in a following wind it may be slightly down by the stern. In any case, down by the stern is usually preferable to being down by the bow, so it is usual to err slightly that way when loading.

Chapter 14

SAILING

PROBABLY the fascination about sailing is that you are always learning. It is always possible to get better at it. As well as this there is the thrill of using your skill to harness the wind to do your bidding. When you get to your destination or win a race, it is you that has done it. The much-quoted saying of Water Rat about the joys of messing about in boats can be taken a step further if the boat is one you have built yourself and an even further step if it is a sailing boat. In this highly mechanized age, a cruise or race in a boat propelled by the wind gives that rare feeling of achievement and satisfaction, not so easily acquired in any other activity.

Although it is always possible to learn more about sailing, it is quite easy to acquire the basic knowledge to go afloat and make the boat do what you want. You do not even need an instructor in the boat, although if someone who knows is willing to teach you that is a good thing. However, many boys have learned to sail by reading about it then going afloat and experimenting. This book is mainly about building boats and this chapter is included to tell you how to sail your boat when you have built it. As you get more ambitious you can read about more advanced sailing in books entirely devoted to it. Several of these are listed in Appendix B.

The principles of sailing are best considered in relation to a single-handed boat with just one sail, although a larger craft with more crew and several sails is handled in a similar way. The ideal way to learn is to go afloat on a lake with no obstructions around it to deflect the wind on a day when a steady light breeze is blowing. These conditions are rare, but if you have to choose other waters wait for a light wind for your first solo attempt, otherwise fluky winds or too strong ones may cause trouble before you know how to deal with it.

If the sail is allowed to fly free it will flap like a flag and have little effect on the boat. Remember this. If you do not know what to do next or the boat is taking charge of you, pay out the sheet so that the wind is spilled out of the sail and it is allowed to flap. If you can use the tiller to turn the boat into the wind, the boat will stop and you have time to think. The only time when these actions are difficult is when you are "running" with the wind coming from aft, so although sailing with the wind seems the simplest direction, it is not the best direction to start learning. If you are caught with the wind aft and want to stop, you must turn the boat right round into the wind, going in the direction opposite to that on which the boom is if possible.

If possible start sailing from a windward bank, i.e. the one from which the wind is blowing. Have the boat with its bow pointing into the wind. Hoist the sail and secure the halliard, preferably merely by turns on the cleat, so that it can be cast off easily in emergency. Ship the rudder and fit the tiller. Lower the centre-board or dagger board if there is sufficient depth. If not, have it ready for lowering. See that the sheet is free to run out, and make sure its end cannot tangle around your feet or any obstruction. Cast off and let yourself drift back from the bank.

The boat will sheer one way or the other. Sit on the windward side, with one hand on the tiller and the other holding the sheet. Use the tiller to turn the boat across the wind and haul in the sheet until the boom is coming in towards the corner of the transom (fig. 49 A). Keep the boat on its course with the rudder. This is "reaching" and is the easiest way to sail. If the boat tries to turn away from

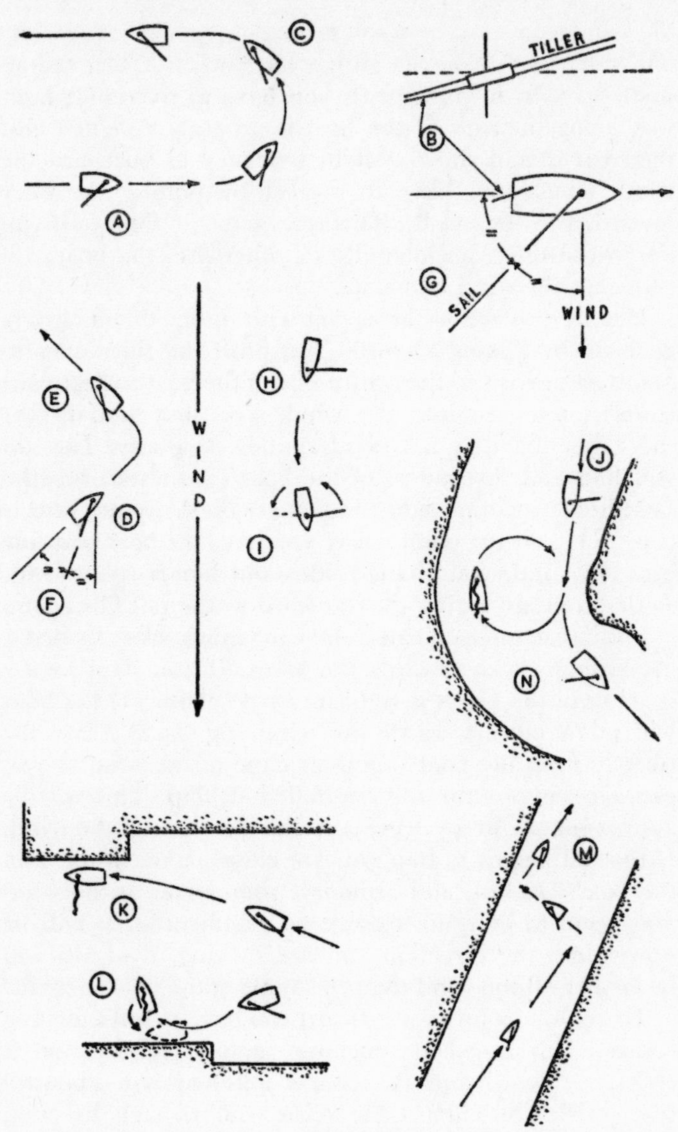

Fig. 49

the wind you may be hauling in the sheet insufficiently, but more likely you are sitting too far aft. When sailing single-handed in most boats you have to sit almost half-way along the side. If the boat is properly designed and rigged it should show a slight tendency to turn into the wind, which you have to correct by pulling the tiller towards you (fig. 49 B). This is a matter of safety—if you let go the tiller, accidentally or otherwise, the boat will turn into the wind and stop.

Having reached as far as you wish in one direction you go back by "going about". You push the tiller over to about 45 degrees to the centre-line of the boat so that your course curves up into the wind. You may pull in the sheet, but this may not be absolutely necessary. The sail will flap and the course of the boat continues until the sail fills on the other side and you are on the return course (fig. 49 C). At the point where you have the boat pointing into the wind, you change sides and hands (photo 28), so that you are sitting to windward as the sail fills again.

From reaching you can change to sailing "close hauled", i.e. sailing closer towards the wind. If you haul in the sheet until the boom is right inboard (photo 31) the boat will point more towards the wind (fig. 49 D). Use the tiller to keep the boat sailing as close to the wind as you can get without the sail beginning to flap. This will be approximately at 45 degrees to the direction of the wind. If the sail begins to flap you are closer to the wind than the boat will sail, and although your angle to the wind may seem to be quite close your actual progress will be slower and the direction you are moving, if at all, will be farther off the wind than the angle of the boat suggests.

To get to a point to windward you have to sail a zig-zag course. This is called "tacking" and each direction is called a "beat" and the course followed is a "board" (fig. 49 E). You sail as close to the wind in each direction as you can, taking care to have enough way on the boat to "go about". If you pinch the boat by trying to get too close to the wind, your speed will be reduced and the boat may not carry enough way to get round as you try to change direction. You may get into the wind and stop there, or even blow backwards. This is called getting "into irons".

Do not worry about this, everyone expects to get caught out in this way occasionally. If the sail does not fill and allow you to get some way on the boat for another attempt, you may have to get out a paddle and pull the boat round.

It may help in sail setting if you consider the theoretical angle of the sail. If you imagine a line for your course and another for the wind crossing through the mast, the average angle of the sail should be bisecting the angle made by these lines (fig. 49 F). As the course and wind lines get closer together so does the sail come nearer to the boat. As the angle widens the sail goes farther out (fig. 49 G). As the sail is not a flat board, the boom has to come in much closer than the theoretical angle to allow for the curve of the sail.

If, instead of turning up into the wind from a reach, the sheet is paid out, the boat will turn away from the wind, at first "broad reaching" (photo 32) then "running" as the wind comes almost aft (fig. 49 H). By then the sail will be let out as far as it will go, probably resting against the shrouds. There will be little sensation of speed unless you look at landmarks, as you are moving with the wind instead of across or against it. This can be deceptive. You may hit something before you realize your progress.

When reaching or tacking you can always stop the boat by turning into the wind, but when running there is no sure way of stopping except by turning completely about so as to bring the boat up into the wind. It is always advisable to make sure you choose a course which will leave you room to do this. How much room you need depends on the boat. A light small boat may almost turn on the spot when the tiller is pushed over. A heavier boat will move more sedately around a larger curve.

Another danger when running is an involuntary "gybe". If you have the wind aft and a puff shifts more to the side on which the boom is, the sail may be taken aback. The boom will lift and swing over to the other side (fig. 49 I). If this is unexpected, you may be hit by it or you may lose balance, and in a bad case the crash may break some of the rigging. When sailing away from the wind it is always best to arrange for the wind to be coming over a quarter, rather than from dead astern (fig. 49 J).

Having learned to control the boat in all possible directions the next thing to do is to apply this knowledge to actual situations. After your sail you will want to get ashore. One way is to turn the boat into the wind in the open water, then lower the sail and row in. To sail in it is a good rule to always try to arrive on a reach. If the landing place is up wind, tack to near it so that you can approach it by reaching (fig. 49 K). To slow the boat as you arrive start spilling air from the sail by easing off the sheet. Spill air, then haul in again briefly to gain a little way, until you finally creep up to the stage. Put your bow into the wind a short distance out and let your sail flap while you prepare to fend the boat off and make fast. A light dinghy stops almost immediately, so you can sail it almost up to the stage before finally spilling the wind. A heavier boat carries its way much longer.

If the landing place is downwind, approach on a reach, spilling the wind to slow the boat in the same way, then turn up into the wind at the last moment to stop the boat and drift back alongside (fig. 49 L).

Tacking in restricted waters may call for long and short boards if the wind is at an angle. It is not always easy to remember that the angle to the wind must be the same both ways when the river banks lead you in another direction. You may find yourself sailing almost along the river on one board, then almost straight across on the other board (fig. 49 M). In this case it is best to concentrate on making all the progress possible on the long

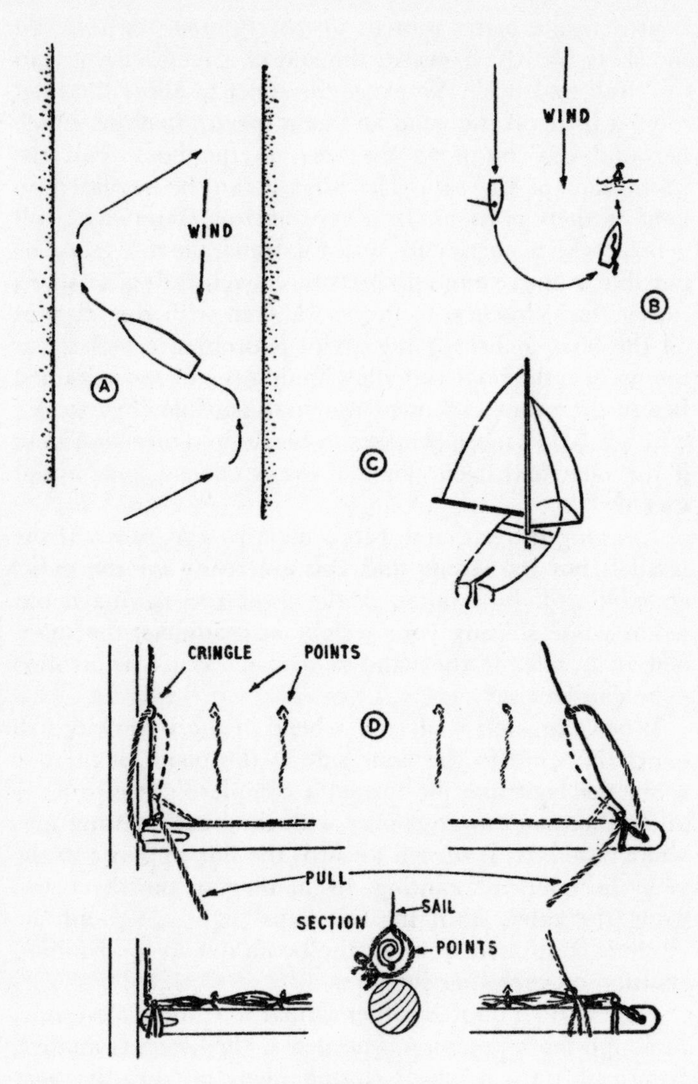

Fig. 50

boards, while being content to merely cross the river on the short boards. Towards the end of a long leg you can sail "full and bye". You ease the sheet to allow the boat to go a little off the wind and gain speed, then you pinch her and rely more on the way on the boat than the propulsion of the sail. The process can be repeated so long as there is room. In a very narrow waterway, with a boat which carries its way for some time, it may be possible to make more progress by concentrating on speed rather than closeness to the wind, then with the impetus on the boat to help going about is prolonged as long as the way on the boat will allow so that the distance gained before the other tack is as much as possible (fig. 50 A), with probably more progress in the desired direction than if the boat had been closer to the wind and gone about quickly.

Running in restricted waters may involve gybes. If the wind is not too strong and you are ready for the gybe, controlling it by hauling in the sheet and paying it out again while shifting your weight in readiness, the manoeuvre is safe. If the wind is strong, even a controlled gybe can be risky.

When the wind is aft and a bend in the waterway will bring the wind to the same side as the boom, if there is room the boat may be turned a complete circle so as to allow the boom to cross over with the boat pointing into wind. The boat is turned towards the side opposite to the way the boom is pointing, by hauling in the sheet and using the tiller, until the sail flaps (fig. 49 N) and the circle is continued to bring the boom out to the running position on the other side.

Picking up a buoy is rather similar to coming alongside, although more precision is needed as the target is smaller. Approach on a reach or close hauled and stop the boat by spilling the wind gradually as you arrive. It is easier to see the buoy if you keep it on the same side as you are sitting. If you have a crew, he grabs the buoy. If you are alone, you will have to time things so that the boat arrives without excess way and you can get forward and grab the buoy (fig. 50 B). If the buoy is picked up from anywhere except forward, the boat will be turned round and attempt to sail away. In any case, as soon as you have secured the buoy drop the sail, or you may find yourself sailing dangerously around the buoy.

In tidal waters you have to consider the relative strength of wind and tide. This is a matter of experience and knowing your boat. If the tide is stronger than the wind and in opposite direction, you may have to head into the tide rather than the wind to stop the boat. With wind and tide together you may find that any progress made by tacking is cancelled by the tide—although you make way through the water you are actually going backwards in relation to the bottom. Then you can only anchor and wait for the tide to turn or slacken, or resort to oars or motor.

If the boat has a jib, this can aid manoeuvring and make a boat sail better. Nearly all small boats to-day are rigged as sloops, with a mainsail and a jib, except for the smallest boats, in which the jib would be so small as to be ineffective. When sailing single-handed the jib sheets may be held by jamb cleats or other quick-release locking devices. Besides changing sides and hands when going about, the jib sheets have to be tended and adjusted to suit the expected conditions. Sometimes the jib is not used when single-handed.

When the crew consists of two people the skipper is the helmsman and it is usual to-day to describe his mate as "crew", which can be confusing, as the name is also used as a collective name for everyone on board a boat. The helmsman controls the tiller and the main sheet. The crew tends the jib sheets and adjusts the centreboard. When single-handed sailing, the centre-board may be left down all the time, but there is something to be gained by partly raising it when sailing off the wind. With a mate on board this can be adjusted without difficulty.

In general, the angle of the jib should be approximately the same in relation to the wind as the mainsail. When running, with the boom right out, the jib would be blanketed on that side. To give it more effect the crew may pull it out the other side. This is called "goose-winging". It is a help to have a light pole to hold out the sail (fig. 50 C).

It may seem exciting to have a boat heeling until the gunwale is almost under, but sailing boats are designed to sail best when they are upright. In modern lightweight boats the only ballast is provided by the weight of the crew. They must move about so as to keep the boat trimmed correctly. The movement of the helmsman is restricted by his need to control the tiller, but with its extension, he can do much to assist the crew in balancing the boat by sitting up to windward. Sometimes the crew have to get their weight far outboard. To make this possible, toe straps may be provided. In some of the fastest boats, such as sailing canoes, there are sliding sides to allow the weight to be taken even farther outboard. A trapeze from the mast allows the crew to stand out from the gunwale.

Besides keeping the boat upright, the crew should also consider fore-and-aft trim. Helmsman and crew need to sit near the middle of the boat in most light racing dinghies. As any boat gathers speed, its bow tends to rise and the stern to pull down. Bringing the weight forward when reaching or beating counteracts this. When running, the pressure on the sails tends to push down the bow. To counteract this, both members of the crew should move aft. If the sails are goosewinged, they may sit on opposite sides, ready to move in or out to correct any listing.

For use in light airs a boat may be equipped with alternative or extra sails. Yachts and some racing dinghies have spinnakers. There are parachute-shaped sails made of very light material, which are set in place of the jib for downwind sailing in light airs. The spinnaker balloons out ahead, assisted by a pole, and draws the boat along. Setting a spinnaker and keeping it drawing properly can be a tricky job for the crew.

To give additional sail area in light airs there may be a larger jib, called a genoa. This overlaps the mainsail considerably, but when reaching, in particular, this sail provides extra power.

In the other direction, the standard rig may be found to be too much and a smaller sail area is desirable. If the tendency to list cannot be controlled by the weight of the crew, this is a sign that too much canvas is being carried. Of course, easing the sheets reduces the power of the wind, and extra-strong puffs can be dealt with in this way,but if the whole wind is found to be too much, then sail should be reduced. A racing sailing dinghy may have more than one suit of sails, of different sizes, and one is chosen before launching in anticipation of the weather to come. One way of reducing sail is to lower the jib. In most small boats the crew may have to move to allow for the different trim. If your destination is downwind, it is possible to lower the mainsail and get there under jib only, but with this sail alone there is a limit to the control of direction and the boat cannot be turned up into the wind.

Most boats are equipped with some means of reefing the main sail. This means reducing its area. In many dinghies roller-reefing is used. The boom has a plate with a square hole, into which a spike on the gooseneck fits (photo 26). The square part matches the hole, but if the boom is partly withdrawn, the hole comes over the round part and can be rotated. To reef with this arrangement, the boat is turned into the wind and the halliard slackened. The boom is pulled back and the sail wrapped around the boom by turning it. When sufficient has been taken up the boom is pushed back. Of course, the sheet has to be attached to the end of the boom, and if there is a kicking strap it has to be fixed to jaws which come outside the rolled sail.

Traditional reefing is done with a row of "points" (fig. 50 D). The sail is lowered slightly, then the reef pendant at the tack fastened down. The clew is then pulled down. It is these end fastenings which take the strain. After both ends are secured, the reef points are used to gather up the surplus canvas at the bottom, by tying with reef knots below the sail, but above the boom.

Chapter 15

CRUISING

WHILE there can be much pleasure to be got from rowing a boat on a lake or local river; using an outboard motor boat in canal, river or harbour; or sailing alone or racing on your own waterway: there comes a time when most owners of boats want to go farther afield. The urge may be to make a coastal passage, or even to go foreign in a suitable boat; or the intention may be a more modest inland voyage on canals and rivers.

For all of this, knowledge more than the mere ability to handle the boat is required. Inland the seamanship required is not great, but the coastal sailor has to have more than a smattering of many subjects if he is to tackle his cruise in safety. Books have been published devoted to these many aspects of boating and the names of some of them are given in Appendix B. This chapter can only provide an introduction.

For inland cruising the small boat enthusiast needs to know where he is permitted to go. In many countries the waterways are regarded as national property and those which are navigable are rights of way. In Britain the position is not so simple. Tidal waters may be regarded as public rights of way. You may take your boat on tidal waters, around the coast and up inlets and estuaries as far as the tide reaches, without asking permission or paying a fee, except that in some harbours you are expected to take heed of the directions of the harbourmaster and may have to pay small harbour dues.

Inland, in Britain, ownership of many waterways goes with the ownership of the land adjoining. This applies to rivers and lakes. In law, the owner of the banks also owns the bed of the river and you have no more right over that than you have over the owner's dry land. However, in the same way that public rights of way have been established over private land, rights of way exist on many inland waterways, particularly those that have been used over the centuries for navigation, such as the Severn, Trent, Wye, Stratford Avon and many more. If locks are provided, you may have to pay lock fees, but you do not pay to use the rivers. Some of the larger lakes, such as Windermere and Loch Lomond, have become public rights of way through long usage.

On some other rivers there may be no legal right of way, but boating may be permitted. An attempt should be made to find out about a waterway you intend to visit. Information is available on most of them (see Appendix B), but if you are unsuccessful and still decide to visit a waterway, remember that if anyone protests, they are almost certainly right.

Canals are man-made. The majority are controlled by British Waterways (see Appendix A) from whom a permit must be obtained in advance. In general canals are useful connecting links, although some of them are attractive waterways in their own rights. It is the number of locks rather than the number of miles which controls canal progress. Reservoirs are also man-made and therefore owned by someone from whom permission must be obtained before using them. On those where boating is permitted, it is usually restricted to members of a particular club.

The River Thames is an exception to the rules. Downriver of Teddington it is tidal and free. Upriver of there it is controlled by the Thames Conservancy, who make a charge for a licence as well as for the use of each lock. This is not a cheap river, but it is very popular.

There is no overall licensing of boats and they do not have to be registered, except on a few waterways, such as the Broads, where they are numbered. There is no equivalent of a driving licence and there is no age limit

29. Completion of a full stroke.

30. Corrib at her optimum speed with a small outboard motor.

31. Wensum sailing close to the wind, with sheets hauled in and crew to windward.

32. Wensum broad reaching in a light breeze.

for those in charge of a boat. Restrictions are few, and are mostly concerned with the avoidance of being a nuisance to others, e.g. high-speed craft are not welcome in restricted waters. On some waters there are special regulations made by the controlling authority, but in general all boats are expected to be used in compliance with the International Rules for the Prevention of Collisions at Sea. In law these are as applicable to small boats as to liners. As may be expected, the complete rules are comprehensive, but the small boat user can soon grasp the essentials as they apply to him.

If you and another boat are meeting in a way that will cause a collision if you do not alter course, you alter your course to starboard, so as to pass port to port. Port is left and starboard is right when facing forward. This is not quite the same thing as saying "Keep to the right" although you will not be wrong if you do that on a narrow waterway. You may keep to the left, providing you alter course so as to pass port to port when you meet another boat.

Power, which includes rowing boats, gives way to sail, i.e. a sailing boat always has the right of way and other craft keep clear. The only exception is where a large power craft in a restricted fairway could not alter course without risk of going aground. Then the sailing craft keeps clear. It is usual, in any case, for pleasure craft to give working craft a right of way.

The rules applicable to sailing craft meeting are a little more involved. When two sailing craft are on opposite tacks, the one on the port tack (wind from port side) keeps clear. A sailing boat running free keeps clear of one close hauled, or reaching. When two yachts are running free and are liable to collide, the one to windward keeps clear if they have their booms out the same side, or the one with its boom out to starboard keeps clear if they are on opposite sides. An overtaking boat, however it is propelled, keeps clear, and the overtaken one should hold its course until the other boat has passed.

At night a small open boat under oars or sail need only carry a light to show if necessary. A very small boat driven by an outboard motor may do the same, but if it is bigger it is wiser to have the lights specified for larger power craft. Steamers, motor cruisers, and power-driven boats generally, show a red light to port, a green light to starboard and a white light showing forward from a mast. Another white light at deck level shows astern. Larger sailing craft use the red and green side lights, but no white mast light. A tug with a tow of barges shows two or three mast lights.

Larger craft make sound signals with their siren or whistle, and their signal could be intended for you. One blast means I am altering my course to starboard. Two blasts means I am altering my course to port. Three blasts means I am going astern. On the Thames tideway in particular, four blasts followed by one or two means I am going about to starboard or port respectively. A succession of short blasts means you are standing into danger.

Using a boat on the sea calls for some knowledge of tides, otherwise the boatman finds himself in difficulty. He may find it impossible to progress against a foul tide, there may be an impassable expanse of mud between him and the point he wants to land on, or he may run aground on a sandbank far from the shore. With a knowledge of the tides, the water can be made to help progress instead of hinder it.

Around Britain tidal movements occur in cycles of just over twelve hours. For most places one can assume that if it is high water at 8 a.m. it will be high water again at about 8.30 p.m. and the next day at about 9 a.m. Between these high waters (usually written HW) low waters (LW) occur, with the falling tide (ebb tide) lasting longer than the rising tide (the flood tide). In many places ebb lasts for about 7 hours.

The rise and fall is caused by the whole body of water moving. In a very general way the tidal flow around the

British Isles has the flood tide coming from the west and dividing at Land's End, with that going up the west coast turning around the north of Scotland and coming down to meet that travelling up the Channel near the Straits of Dover. Knowing this, a boatman may go along the South Coast from west to east on a flood tide and cover twice the distance he would have done if he had tried to do the journey against an ebb tide. Both ebb and flood run fastest near the middle of their period and the speed tails off towards the slack water which occurs when the direction is changing.

How much the difference in height is between high and low water varies considerably between places. Where the water is pinched in by a narrowing shoreline, as in the Bristol Channel, there can be a difference of as much as 40 feet. Along the more open coastline of Devon it may only be a few feet. The difference is also affected by the state of the moon. At full and new moon the tide rises higher and drops lower to give Spring Tides. Midway between the tidal range is reduced and we get Neap Tides.

Tide tables are available, giving forecasts of the times and heights of tides for various places. Dover is the standard port and constants are provided, which have to be added or subtracted to give the times at other places. Most seaside resorts, popular yachting centres and shipping ports have their own tide tables, either published commercially or available through the town clerk or a yacht club. Coastal newspapers usually give tide times each day. For over-all predictions there are nautical almanacs (see Appendix B) which give complete tidal information as well as much other useful data.

When entering a strange harbour or estuary it is always best to enter on a rising tide. If you touch the bottom you know that you will soon float off, but if it is a falling tide you may be there until the next tide. The tide may be used to lift a boat on to a trailer or to float it off a slipway. In some places launching is only possible a few hours each side of HW. At other times impassable mud may be exposed.

In reasonable weather waves are only a hazard when they are breaking. A light boat will rise and fall with the waves without being in danger, but if the top of a wave is curling over, water may come on board and if you get broadside to it, it may capsize you. A breaking wave may be caused by the wind blowing over its top, but it is more likely to be due to the drag of the shallow bottom close in shore. Consequently, launching through surf is usually a wet performance. The boat has to be got through several breakers while the water is still too shallow for sailing or power, and this usually means at least one of the crew wading. It is better to find shelter. Even in a bay with a wind blowing onshore, one end of the bay is likely to be more sheltered than the other.

Coming in through surf is just as likely to be wet. Many boats are better turned and brought in stern first as the bow is better able to contend with the approaching waves. Much depends on the boat. The important thing is to keep it end-on, otherwise the waves may roll it over when it touches bottom. Sea boating is best approached by preliminary work in sheltered harbours and estuaries.

Besides its normal equipment, already mentioned, any boat that goes to sea should have a second means of propulsion—usually oars. If it is a rowing boat, then there should be spare oars and rowlocks. A canoe paddle will not get a dinghy home against an ebb tide. There should be more than enough lifejackets for the crew and adequate reserve buoyancy in the boat. All of this applies to short trips. If an extended cruise is anticipated, much more is needed, and the instructions on cruising in a book dealing completely with it should be absorbed and followed. Anyone cruising in a small boat has the same problems as the man in charge of a large craft, but his circumstances are mostly more awkward and difficult. True, he may be able to get ashore in places unsuited to the large craft, but he should know where to run at any state of his

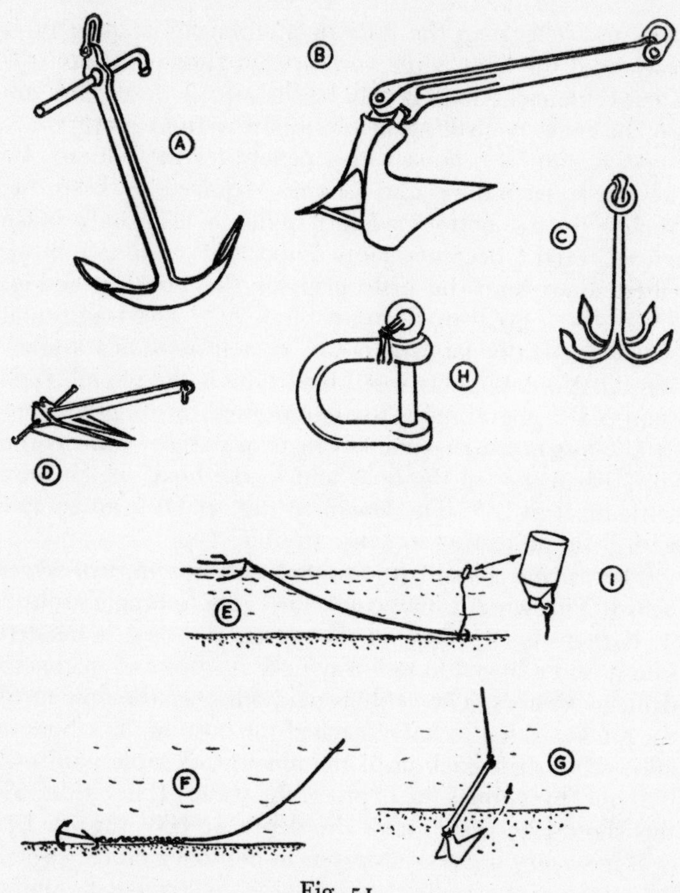

Fig. 51

voyage, if he has to avoid bad weather. Much coast is inhospitable, and the cruising boatman should have advance knowledge of possible landing places. It it no use expecting to read it up when needed—conditions may be such that all your attention is needed dealing with the problem in hand.

An anchor is useful on almost any waters, but it is an essential piece of equipment on tidal waters. Inland you may use it to keep the boat in position for angling or it may hold the boat while you sort out rigging. There it is a convenience. At sea it may be the means of keeping you off the rocks or drifting helplessly away from shore.

An anchor is a hook which penetrates the bottom. Its weight is secondary and is only required to keep the anchor on the bottom while it pulls in. The only place where weight becomes more important is in soft mud, where there may be little grip for the hooking action. There are a great many types of anchor. The traditional one is generally known to-day as a fisherman's anchor (fig. 51 A). A popular small boat type is the plough type (fig. 51 B). A grapnel is sometimes used for dinghies (fig. 51 C), but the many points can be a danger both to the crew when it is in the boat and to the boat, which may settle on it at LW. The Danforth (fig. 51 D) is an anchor with little projecting to cause trouble.

The anchor should be lowered and not thrown overboard. Throwing it may cause the cable to tangle around it. If there is any flow on the water, the boat is headed into it and allowed to lose way until it stops and begins to drift backwards. The cable is paid out over the bow until the anchor is felt to have reached the bottom. The boat is allowed to drift back until the amount of cable paid out is about three times the depth of the water. If in a tideway this should be three times the depth at HW (fig. 51 E).

If necessary use power or oars to pull back on the cable. The stock of the anchor, or its shape, will cause the point or fluke to turn downwards and start to dig in (fig. 51 F). As the boat pulls on the cable, the anchor will dig in deeper. To break out the anchor the cable is pulled in until the cable is near vertical. Further pulling will cause the fluke to dig its way to the surface (fig. 51 G) and come clear. Once the anchor is free of the bottom the boat may begin to move and you must be prepared to handle it, so it may be necessary to start sailing, rowing or motoring before your crew actually has the anchor on board.

In a small boat it is usual to have rope for the anchor cable. This is buoyant and does not do anything to help the anchor to bite. It is a big help to have a length of chain between the rope and the anchor, as its weight keeps the curve of the cable lower and the pull on the anchor is more nearly horizontal. The rope can be spliced around a thimble and shackled to the chain, which is also shackled to the anchor, but as you cannot inspect the fastenings once the anchor is lowered and any failure means the loss of the anchor, the screwed pin in the shackle should be secured with copper wire (fig. 51 H).

When anchored in a tideway, allow for the boat swinging as the tide turns. In a much-used harbour or other congested place there may be a real risk of the anchor getting foul of a sunken cable or other solid obstruction so that pulling on the anchor cable will not release it. If the water is too deep for diving, the only way out may be to cut the cable and lose the anchor. To guard against this there may be an anchor buoy (fig. 51 I). This need only be a can on a light line, but it is attached to the anchor at a point that will withdraw the fluke the way it went in. If your anchor fails to come free by pulling on its cable you have a second chance by pulling on the buoy line.

Another esssential item for coastwise cruising is a compass used with a chart. The wise seaman always knows where he is, so that if a mist comes down he can navigate to a safe destination. There are many compasses, but nothing elaborate is needed for dinghy cruising. The most useful type is a hand-bearing pattern. With this landmarks may be sighted and the bearing read off. The same compass can be used to steer by. Admiralty charts are intended for larger craft, but there are several yachtsman's charts published by the Admiralty and other makers, which simplify things by using colour and giving bearings of common courses. There are also pilot books published covering popular boating areas, which contain all the vital information in compact form. The appropriate books and charts should be obtained before a cruise and studied thoroughly, so that any reference to them while afloat is more in the nature of a reminder than a search for new information.

Navigation and pilotage is outside the scope of this book, but there are many good books on the subject (see Appendix B).

A cruise in a small boat in open waters is not a project to be tackled lightly. If a mistake is made, there may not be a second chance. The sea is unpredictable. A trip of a few hours in a bay or harbour is a very different thing from setting off for a destination involving open sea, even if it is only a coastwise hop of a few hours. A boat which is suitable for inland use or even for harbour use is not necessarily suitable for the sort of sea which can spring up even in apparently settled weather. No doubt many readers of this book will eventually go to sea, but before venturing out they will first train in a seamanlike way by becoming proficient in all the arts of a seaman in estuaries, harbours, sea lochs and similar places. There is plenty of scope for adventurous boating in such large expanses of tidal water as Poole and Chichester Harbours. A good seaman is one who anticipates every possible contingency and knows what he would do every time. He sees that his boat is sound and properly equipped. He is careful and painstaking over everything to do with his craft and her use. All equipment has a place and is returned there. He is never reckless. If he thinks some venture is risky, he thinks out everything which might go wrong. If he cannot see a way of dealing with the emergency, he does not tackle the venture.

There is a tremendous satisfaction to be got from all kinds of boating, but the good boatman takes care never to put himself into a position where he could be a danger to himself or others, or cause others to get into danger because of his own foolishness.

APPENDIX A

Organizations of interest to boat builders and users

Royal Yachting Association, 171 Victoria Street, London, S.W.1.

This is the national body to which all the dinghy racing clubs are affiliated. It looks after the interests of yachtsmen and represents this country in international matters.

Central Council of Physical Recreation, 6 Bedford Square, London, W.C.1.

This body organises sailing courses on a national and local scale and its representatives are able to help schools, youth organizations and similar bodies. Details of courses may be obtained from head office or from any of the regional offices:

WELSH OFFICES: 52 Charles Street, Cardiff.
16 Chester Street, Wrexham.
NORTHERN IRELAND OFFICE: 45 Arthur Street, Belfast.
ENGLISH REGIONS:
NORTH-EAST: 40 Saddler Street, Durham City.
YORKSHIRE: 4 Albion Street, Leeds.
NORTH MIDLANDS: Bank Chambers, 125 St. Ann's Well Road, Nottingham.
EAST: 5a Harpur Street, Bedford.
LONDON AND SOUTH-EAST: 6 Bedford Square, London, W.C.1.
SOUTH: Watlington House, Reading.
SOUTH-WEST: 29 Market Street, Crewkerne.
WEST MIDLANDS: 256 Moseley Road, Birmingham 12.
NORTH-WEST: 26 Brazenose Street, Manchester 2.

Scottish Council of Physical Recreation, 4 Queensferry Street, Edinburgh 2.

This is the Scottish equivalent of the C.C.P.R. organizing similar activities in Scotland.

Inland Waterways Association, 4 Emerald Street, London, W.C.1.

This body is mainly concerned with protecting the interests and rights of those who wish to use the inland waters for any purpose. It is not primarily a supplier of waterways information.

British Canoe Union, 147a Station Road, London, E.4.

Although not an organization for those using craft other than canoes, the B.C.U. is of interest as they probably have a greater store of waterways information than any other body.

Ship and Boat Builders' National Federation, 23 Knightsbridge, London, S.W.1.

This is the national assocation of professional boat-builders.

Royal National Lifeboat Institution, 42 Grosvenor Gardens, London, S.W.1.

This institution depends on voluntary contributions and support should be given by all who go to sea.

Timber Development Association, 21 College Hill, London, E.C.4.

This body can provide authoratative information on the uses of various woods in boatbuilding.

British Waterways, Melbury House, Melbury Terrace, London, N.W.1.

A licence must be obtained from them before using any of the national canal system. The country is divided approximately North and South, and East and West through a point North of Birmingham and application should be made, if possible to the office in a particular region:

S.W. DIVISION (British Waterways, 16 Bridge Street, Broad Street, Birmingham 1).

S.E. DIVISION (British Waterways, "Willow Grange", Church Road, Watford, Herts.).

N.E. DIVISION (British Waterways, P.O. Box 9, 1 Dock Street, Leeds 1).

N.W. DIVISION (British Waterways, Lime Street Chambers, Lime Street, Liverpool 1).

Port and Haven Commissioners, 21 South Quay, Great Yarmouth.

This is the authority controlling the Norfolk and Suffolk Broads. A permit must be obtained from them for the use of these waters.

Thames Conservancy Board, 2 and 3 Norfolk Street, Strand, London, W.C.2.

A licence must be obtained from them before using the River Thames upriver of Teddington Lock.

APPENDIX B

Publications of interest to boat builders and users.

There are a very large number of books dealing with all aspects of boating, published in Britain and elsewhere. Those listed here are a representative selection of some known to the author which, at the time of writing, are either in print or not very long out of print. A bookseller or librarian can trace a book if he knows the title, author and publisher. Many books published in one country are available through other publishers who represent them in other countries. As prices vary, none are quoted, but as some guide to the size of the book, letters are used to indicate the group into which the book falls. "S" indicates a small book, usually paper-backed. "M" indicates a book of medium size, roughly comparable in size and price with the present volume. "L" indicates a large book, costing upwards of twice the price of this one, and either much thicker or with a larger page size. The books are not listed in any particular order.

Other relevant books by P. W. Blandford:

Boat Building (Foyle) S.
Building and Sailing Catamarans (Foyle) S.
Boatswain and Boatswain Mate Badge (Brown, Son & Ferguson) S.
Scouting on the Water (Jenkins) M.
Canoes and Canoeing (Lutterworth) M.
Tackle Canoeing This Way (Stanley Paul) M.
Tackle Trailer Boating This Way (Stanley Paul) M.
Your Book of Knots (Faber) M.
Rope Splicing (Brown, Son & Ferguson) S.
Netmaking (Brown, Son & Ferguson) S.
Getting Afloat—annually (Link House) S.

Boat building books:

Complete Amateur Boat Building, by Verney (Murray) M.
Boatbuilding, by Chapelle (Norton, U.S.A.) L.
Hartley's Guide to Boat Building (Imray & Wilson) M.
Boatbuilding from Kits, by Mason (Coles) S.
Design and Construction of Small Craft (Trundall) M.
Glass Fibre for Amateurs, Lewis and Warring (Model Aeronautical Press) S.
Lifeboat into Yacht, by Verney (Yachting Monthly) S.
Practical Yacht Construction, by Watts (Coles) L.
Make Your Own Sails, by Bowker and Budd (Macmillan) M.
Sailing Yacht Design, by Birt (Coles) L.

Seamanship books:

Small Boat Manual, by Warring (Stanley Paul) L.
Beginner's Guide to the Sea, by Knight (Macmillan) M.
Coastwise Navigation, by Watkins (Kandy) S.
Coastal Navigation Wrinkles, by Rantzen (Coles) S.
Celestial Navigation, by Blewett (Iliffe) S.
An Introduction to Charts and Their Uses, by Chriss and Hayes (Brown, Son & Ferguson) M.
Seamanship, by Hoyt (Darton, Longman & Todd) M.
Seamanship Handbook, by Bonwick (Geo. Philip) M.
Boatswain's Manual, by McLeod (Brown, Son & Ferguson) M.
Sea Signalling Simplified, by Russell (Coles) S.
Yacht Racing Rules Simplified, by Somerville (Coles) S.
Ashley Book of Knots, by Ashley (Doubleday Doran, U.S.A.) L.
Knots and Splices, by Day (Coles) S.
Knots, Splices and Fancy Work, by Spencer (Brown, Son & Ferguson) M.

Sailing books:

Starting to Sail, by Fisher (Coles) S.
Sailing Dinghies, by Fisher (Coles) S.
Tackle Sailing This Way, by Dawson (Stanley Paul) M.
Sailing, Step by Step, by Knights (Arco) M.
Small Boat Sailing, by Morgan (Foyle) S.
Sailing, by Tetley (Stanley Paul) L.
Teach Yourself Sailing, by Lewis (Oxford U.P.) M.
Dinghy Sailing Simply Explained, by Prout (Brown, Son & Ferguson) S.
Offshore, by Illingworth (Coles) L.
The Science of Sailing, by Robinson (Macmillan) L.
The New Small Boat Sailing, by Fisher (Coles) M.
Dinghy Ownership, by Nightingale (Coles) M.
Better Small Boat Sailing, by Fisher (Coles) M.
Sailing Boats, by Uffa Fox (Newnes) M.
Dinghy Year Book—annually (Coles) M.

Sailing Primer, by Park (Bell) M.
Sailing for Beginners, by Hunter (Nelson) M.

Pilot and guide books:
Reed's Nautical Almanac—annually (Reed) L.
Brown's Nautical Almanac—annually (Brown, Son & Ferguson) L.
Pilot to the South Coast Harbours, by Coles (Faber) M.
Pilot's Guide to the English Channel, by Wilson and Branson (Imray & Wilson) L.
West Country Rivers (Yachting Monthly) S.
East Coast Rivers (Yachting Monthly) S.
British Canoe Union, Guide to the Waterways of the British Isles (B.C.U.) M.
Inland Waterways of Great Britain and Northern Ireland, by Edwards (Imray & Wilson) L.

British Waterways publish a series of guide books:

1 *Llangollen Canal.*
2 *Trent Waterway.*
3 *Lee and Stort Navigations.*
4 *Staffordshire and Worcestershire Canal.*
5 *Shropshire Union Canal.*
6 *Oxford Canal.*
7 *Fossdyke and Witham Navigations.*
8 *Grand Union Canal*, part 1, Regents Canal Dock, Brentford, to Braunston.
9 *Grand Union Canal*, part 2, Braunston to Birmingham, with Parts of Other Canals.
10 *Grand Union Canal*, part 3, Norton Junction to Trent Lock.
11 *Macclesfield Canal.*
12 *Trent and Mersey Canal*, part 1, Trent Lock to Great Haywood and Parts of Other Canals.
13 *Trent and Mersey Canal*, part 2, Preston Brook to Great Haywood and Parts of Other Canals.
14 *Severn Waterway.*

Charts and maps:

Admiralty Charts (Admiralty, or agents).
Yachtsman's charts (Imray & Wilson).
Yachtsman's charts (Edward Stanford).
Ordnance Survey Maps (H.M.S.O. or agents).
Inland Cruising Map (Edward Stanford).
Canoeist's Map (Edward Stanford).
Stanford's Map of the Broads (Edward Stanford).
Stanford's Map of the Thames (Edward Stanford).
Map of Fenland rivers (Lincoln, Ely).
Blake's Map of the Broads (Blake).
Chart of the Severn and Avon (Jones, Birmingham).
Hamilton's chart and index of the Broads (Hamilton, Oulton Broad).

General books:

Motor Boat and Yachting Manual (Temple Press) M.
Manual of Seamanship (H.M.S.O.) L.
Boatman's Manual, by Lane (Norton, U.S.A.) M.
According to Uffa, by Uffa Fox (Newnes) M.
Expert's Book of Boating, by Brindze (Kaye) L.
Fast Boats, by Teal (Temple Press) M.
High Speed Small Craft, by du Cane (Temple Press) L.
Safety in Small Boats, by Rayner (Coles) M.

Periodicals:

Light Craft (monthly).
Yachts and Yachting (fortnightly).
Yachting World (monthly).
Motor Boat and Yachting (fortnightly).
Yachting Monthly (monthly).
The Yachtsman (monthly).

INDEX